Contents

KU-603-986

Building Regulations 1997
Technical Guidance Document B - Fire Safety

Introduction

This document has been published by the Minister for the Environment under article 7 of the Building Regulations, 1997. It provides guidance in relation to Part B of the Second Schedule to the Regulations. The document should be read in conjunction with the Building Regulations, 1997, and other documents published under these Regulations.

In general, Building Regulations apply to the construction of new buildings and to extensions and material alterations to buildings. In addition, certain parts of the Regulations apply to existing buildings where a material change of use takes place. Otherwise, Building Regulations do not apply to buildings constructed prior to 1 June, 1992.

Transitional Arrangements

In general, this document applies to works, or buildings in which a material change of use takes place, where the works or the change of use commence or takes place, as the case may be on or after 1 January, 1998. Technical Guidance Document B - FIRE, dated 1991, also ceases to have effect from that date. However, the latter document may continue to be used in the case of works, or buildings in which a material change of use takes place -

- where the works or the change of use commence or takes place, as the case may be, before 1 January, 1998,

- in respect of which a Fire Safety Certificate under the Building Control Regulations, 1991 to 1994, has been granted, where the works or change of use commence or takes place, as the case may be, not later than 31 December, 2002.

The Guidance

The materials, methods of construction, standards and other specifications (including technical specifications) which are referred to in this document are those which are likely to be suitable for the purposes of the Regulations. Where works are carried out in accordance with the guidance in this document, this will, prima facie, indicate compliance with Part B of the Second Schedule of the Building Regulations. However, the adoption of an approach other than that outlined in the guidance is not precluded provided that the relevant requirements of the Regulations are complied with. Those involved in the design and construction of a building may be required by the relevant building control authority to provide such evidence as is necessary to establish that the requirements of the Building Regulations have been complied with. In the case of an application for a fire safety certificate under the Building Control Regulations, it is necessary to demonstrate compliance with Part B of the Second Schedule to the Building Regulations.

Existing Buildings

In the case of material alterations or changes of use of existing buildings, the adoption of the guidance in this document without modification may not, in all circumstances, be appropriate. In particular, the adherence to guidance including codes, standards or technical specifications, intended for application to new work may be unduly restrictive or impracticable. Buildings of architectural or historical interest are especially likely to give rise to such circumstances. In these situations, alternative approaches based on the principles contained in the document may be more relevant and should be considered.

Technical Specifications

Building Regulations are made for specific purposes, e.g. to provide, in relation to buildings, for the health, safety and welfare of persons, the conservation of energy and access for disabled persons. Technical specifications (including harmonised European Standards, European Technical Approvals, National Standards and Agrément Certificates) are relevant to the extent that they relate to these considerations. Any reference to a technical specification is a reference to so much of the specification as is relevant in the context in which it arises. Technical specifications may also address other aspects not covered by the Regulations.

A reference to a technical specification is to the latest edition (including any amendments, supplements or addenda) current at the date of publication of this Technical Guidance Document. However, if this version of the technical specification is subsequently revised or updated by the issuing body, the new version may be used as a source of guidance provided that it continues to address the relevant requirements of the Regulations.

Materials and Workmanship

Under Part D of the Second Schedule to the Building Regulations, works to which the regulations apply must be carried out with proper materials and in a workmanlike manner. Guidance in relation to compliance with this requirements is contained in Technical Guidance Document D.

Interpretation

In this document, a reference to a section, sub-section, part, paragraph or diagram is, unless otherwise stated, a reference to a section, sub-section, part, paragraph or diagram, as the case may be, of this document. A reference to another Technical Guidance Document is a reference to the latest edition of a document published by the Minister for the Environment under article 7 of the Building Regulations, 1997. Diagrams are used in this document to illustrate particular aspects of construction - they may not show all the details of construction.

Fire Safety
Building Regulations - The Requirement

Part B of the Second Schedule to the Building Regulations, 1997, provides as follows:

Means of escape in case of fire.	**B1**	A building shall be so designed and constructed that there are adequate means of escape in case of fire from the building to a place of safety outside the building, capable of being safely and effectively used.
Internal fire spread (linings).	**B2**	For the purpose of inhibiting the spread of fire within a building, the internal linings - (a) shall offer adequate resistance to the spread of flame over their surfaces; and (b) shall have, if ignited, a rate of heat release which is reasonable in the circumstances.
Internal fire spread (structure).	**B3**	(1) A building shall be so designed and constructed that, in the event of fire, its stability will be maintained for a reasonable period. (2) (a) A wall common to two or more buildings shall be so designed and constructed that it offers adequate resistance to the spread of fire between those buildings. (b) A building shall be sub-divided with fire resisting construction where this is necessary to inhibit the spread of fire within the building. (3) A building shall be so designed and constructed that the unseen spread of fire and smoke within concealed spaces in its structure or fabric is inhibited where necessary. (4) For the purposes of sub-paragraph 2(a), a house in a terrace and a semi-detached house are each to be treated as being a separate building.
External fire spread.	**B4**	The external walls and roof of a building shall be so designed and constructed that they afford adequate resistance to the spread of fire to and from neighbouring buildings.
Access and facilities for the fire service.	**B5**	A building shall be so designed and constructed that there is adequate provision for access for fire appliances and for such other facilities as may be reasonably required to assist the fire service in the protection of life and property.

Section B0
Fire Safety

0.1 Use of the Guidance

Arrangements of Sections

0.1.1 The provisions set out in Sections B1 to B5 of this Document, deal with different aspects of fire safety. The five sections, in addition to this one dealing with general provisions, are :

B1	Means of escape in case of fire
B2	Internal fire spread (linings)
B3	Internal fire spread (structure)
B4	External fire spread
B5	Access and facilities for the fire service

B1 aims to ensure that a satisfactory standard of means of escape is provided for persons in the event of fire in a building;

B2 aims to ensure that fire spread over the internal linings of buildings is inhibited;

B3 aims to ensure the stability of buildings in the event of fire, that there is a sufficient degree of fire separation within buildings and between adjoining buildings, and to inhibit the unseen spread of fire and smoke in concealed spaces in buildings;

B4 aims to ensure that external walls and roofs have adequate resistance to the spread of fire over their external surfaces, and that spread of fire from one building to another is restricted; and

B5 aims to ensure satisfactory access for fire appliances to buildings and facilities in buildings to assist fire fighters in the protection of life and property.

Interaction of Provisions

0.1.2 Whilst provisions appropriate to B1 to B5 are set out separately in this Document, many of the provisions are closely interlinked. For example, there is a close link between the provisions for means of escape (B1) and those for the control of fire growth (B2), fire containment (B3), and facilities for the fire service (B5). Similarly there are links between B3 and the provisions for controlling external fire spread (B4), and between B3 and B5. Interaction between these different requirements should be recognised where variations in the standard of provision are being considered. A higher standard under one of the requirements may be of benefit in respect of one or more of the other requirements. Thus the provisions in the Document as a whole should be considered as a package aimed at achieving an acceptable standard of fire safety.

Performance Statements

0.1.3 At the start of Sections B1 to B5, the relevant requirement of the Regulations is set out and is followed by a performance statement which indicates how the requirement may be met. These statements incorporate the essential elements required to satisfy the Regulations and form the basis for the provisions contained in the guidance.

Alternative Solutions

0.1.4 The detailed provisions set out in this Document are intended to provide guidance for some of the more common building situations. In other situations, alternative ways of achieving compliance with the requirements of Part B of the Second Schedule to the Building Regulations may be appropriate. There is no obligation to adopt any particular solution contained herein. The use of alternative design solutions, standards, systems or methods of fire protection to those outlined in this document are acceptable, provided the level of fire safety achieved is adequate to satisfy the requirements of the Building Regulations.

Alternative approaches (see 0.2) based on fire safety engineering may be employed to satisfy the requirements of the Regulations. These may be based on a fundamental analysis of the fire safety problem or involve a comparative analysis between a provision of this technical guidance document and an alternative solution. Where appropriate, compensating fire safety measures should be considered and evaluated. A qualitative assessment of the alternative design may be adequate in some cases, but generally quantitative analysis will also be required.

Existing Buildings

0.1.5 In the case of an existing building there may be constraints that would not exist with a new building and some variation of the provisions set out in this Document may be appropriate. Alternative solutions (see 0.1.4), whether applied to all or part of the building or to specific provisions, may be employed in these situations.

Many fire safety provisions are inter-dependant and should not be considered in isolation. Where a particular provision outlined in this Document can not be practicably achieved, account may be taken of compensating fire safety measures, depending on the nature and circumstances of each particular case. Such measures would include active and/or passive provisions. Active provisions are those which come into action on detection of fire (such as fire suppression systems) while passive provisions relate to the defence against fire provided by the fabric and construction of a building (such as floors and walls).

A number of useful publications are available which outline alternative approaches to fire safety in existing buildings of special or historic merit. These include:

- Fire protection in old buildings and historic town centres, published by the Fire Protection Association;

- Fire protection measures for the Royal Palaces, Department of National Heritage, London; and

- Heritage under fire, a guide to the protection of historic buildings by the United Kingdom Working Party on Fire Safety in historic buildings.

Fire Safety Management

0.1.6 Whilst the provisions of the Building Regulations do not relate to the management of fire safety in buildings, it would be appropriate and prudent to consider the importance of this aspect to the overall fire safety of a building. The guidance contained in this Document has been based on the assumption that there will be an adequate level of fire safety management when the building is in use.

Active fire safety measures, such as automatic fire detection and alarms systems, smoke control systems or automatic suppression systems, may play a critical role in the fire safety strategy of a building. The management of such systems during the life of the building is an important consideration.

The management of passive systems, which include the fire protection provided by the fabric and construction of the building (including components such as fire doors, shutters, dampers, etc.) is also important, to ensure that deterioration over the life of a building will not impair the level of fire safety.

Attention is drawn to duties under the Fire Services Act, 1981 in relation to the use of certain premises. Attention is also drawn to duties under the Safety, Health and Welfare at Work Act, 1989 in relation to a place of work as defined in that legislation.

0.2. Alternative Approaches to Fire Safety requirements

0.2.1 Rigid compliance with the provisions set out in this document might prove unduly restrictive in the design of some large and complex buildings. A fire safety engineering approach that takes into account the total fire safety package can provide an alternative approach to providing fire safety. In such cases it would be appropriate to take into account a range of fire safety features, some of which are dealt with in this Document, and some of which are not addressed in any detail, and to set these against an assessment of the hazard and risk peculiar to the particular case.

Fire safety engineering may also be used to demonstrate the adequacy of alternative solutions to those outlined in this Technical Guidance Document. This approach may also be appropriate in the case of existing buildings or where a particular provision of the guidance can not practicably be achieved.

0.2.2 Factors that should be taken into account include:

- the risk of a fire occurring,
- the resulting fire severity,
- the fire safety measures provided, and
- the risk to persons in the event of a fire occurring.

0.2.3 A wide variety of measures could be considered and incorporated to a greater or lesser extent, as appropriate to the circumstances. These include:

- the adequacy of the means to prevent fires occurring,
- early warning by automatic fire detection and alarm systems,
- the means of escape provided,
- provision of smoke control systems,
- control of the rate of growth of a fire,
- the adequacy of the structure to resist the effects of a fire,
- the degree of fire containment,
- fire separation between buildings or parts of buildings,
- the standard of active measures for fire extinguishment or control,
- facilities to assist the fire service,
- the degree of fire safety management including the likely standard of maintenance of the fire safety systems,
- consideration of the availability of any continuing control under other legislation that could ensure continued maintenance of such systems.

0.2.4 A fire safety engineering approach can provide a more fundamental solution than traditional prescriptive approaches to fire safety. It may be the only viable means of achieving a satisfactory standard of fire safety in some large and complex buildings. Shopping centres (see 3.5.3) or large buildings containing atria (see 3.5.5) are examples of where this approach can be used.

The fire safety engineering design process includes a qualitative assessment of the design, a quantified analysis and a comparison with defined safety criteria.

The adequacy of the fire safety design should be assessed on the basis of appropriate life safety criteria, using the following alternative approaches:

(a) a probabilistic or risk-based approach;

(b) a deterministic approach, which establishes the worst credible fire scenarios to be considered in detail, with the addition of appropriate safety factors; or

(c) a comparison of the performance of a proposed alternative solution with that achieved using the guidance in this technical guidance document.

In the case of a fundamental analysis and depending on the life risks involved, the uncertainties in the initial assumptions and the design procedures used, safety factors are required to ensure an adequate level of safety.

In the case of a comparative analysis, inherent or implied safety factors could be used to ensure that the design adopted will provide a level of safety at least equivalent to that achieved by the use of a prescribed design solution.

In the case of a probabilistic risk assessment the likelihood of a given event occurring should be shown to be acceptably low. The life risk analysis involves considering the probability of a fire starting and heat and smoke spreading to produce untenable conditions in an occupied part of the building. Comparative risk assessment studies may be used to show that an alternative design solution is at least as safe as that achieved by a prescribed design solution.

Further guidance on fire safety engineering principles is contained in The Society of Fire Protection Engineers Handbook of Fire Protection Engineering.

Suitable references to other guidance material are also contained in many of the codes of practice and other documents referred to in Section B1 (1.1) of this Technical Guidance Document.

0.2.5 Fire is a complex phenomenon and there are on-going developments in the field of fire safety engineering to improve the understanding of fire behaviour and its consequences.

Many analytical models, which are based on mathematical relationships necessary for a set of fire conditions to exist, have been developed. Computer-based models are now also available to predict the behaviour of fire and its consequences. Care should be exercised in the use of fire models, to ensure the validity of the results. An understanding of the parameters, assumptions and limitations of the model, the accuracy and proper application of the input data and the correct interpretation of the output, is always required.

Guidance on fire modelling and its application is available in the following publications:

- Building Research Establishment Report (BR223) Mathematical fire modelling and its application to fire safety design;
- Building Research Establishment Digest 367, 1991 Fire modelling;
- Fire Models, A Guide for Fire Prevention Officers, Fire Research and Development Group (BT Hume).

0.3 Provisions common to Sections B1 to B5

0.3.1 Under the provisions in this Document there are a number of items that are common to one or more of the requirements. These include a classification of purpose groups, fire performance of materials and structures, provisions regarding fire doors, methods of measurement, and definitions. For convenience these and other appropriate items have been drawn together for common reference as Appendices to this Document.

Purpose Groups

0.3.2 Many of the provisions in this Document are related to the use of the building. The use classifications are termed purpose groups and from this it follows that the relevant purpose group should be decided before the provisions can be determined.

Purpose groups can apply to a whole building, or (where a building is compartmented) to a compartment in the building, and the relevant purpose group should be taken from the main use of the building or compartment. However, in some situations there may be more than one use involved in a building or compartment, and in certain circumstances it is appropriate to treat the different uses as belonging to a purpose group in its own right. These situations are:

(a) a flat or maisonette;

(b) storage for a shop if the area of storage is more than one-half of the total floor area of the shop; and

(c) in other buildings, any ancillary use if its area is more than one-quarter of the total floor area of the building or part.

Some buildings may have two or more main uses that are not ancillary to one another, for example, offices over shops from which they are independent. In such cases, each of the uses should be considered as belonging to a purpose group in its own right.

In other cases and particularly in some large buildings there may be a complex mix of uses. In such cases it is necessary to consider the possible risk that one part of a complex may have on another and special measures to reduce the risk may be necessary.

Table 0.1 sets out the purpose group classification.

Table 0.1	**Classification of buildings by purpose group**	
Use	**Group**	**Purpose for which a building or compartment of a building is used**
Residential (Dwellings)	1(a)[1]	Dwelling house with no habitable storey with a floor level which is more than 4.5m above ground level.
	1(b)[1]	Dwelling house with a habitable storey with a floor which is more than 4.5 m above ground level.
	1(c)	Flat or maisonette.
Residential (Institutional)	2(a)	Hospital, nursing home, home for old people or for children, school or other similar establishment used as living accommodation or for the treatment, care or maintenance of people suffering from illness or mental or physical disability or handicap, where such people sleep on the premises.
Other Residential	2(b)	Hotel, hostel, guest building, residential college, hall of residence, and any other residential purpose not described above.
Office	3	Premises used for the purpose of administration, clerical work (including writing, book keeping, sorting papers, filing, typing, duplicating, machine calculating, drawing and the editorial preparation of matter for publication, handling money (including banking and building society work), telephone system operation).
Shop	4(a)	Premises used for a retail or wholesale trade or business (including retail sales by auction, self-selection and over-the-counter wholesale trading, the business of lending books or periodicals for gain and the business of a barber or hairdresser) and premises to which the public is invited to deliver or to collect goods in connection with their hire, repair or other treatment, or where they themselves may carry out such repairs or other treatments.
Shopping Centre	4(b)	A building which comprises a number of individually occupied premises to which common access is provided principally for the benefit of shoppers.
Assembly and recreation	5	Place of assembly [2] or recreation, including the following: (i) a theatre, public library, hall or other building of public resort used for social or recreational purposes, (ii) a non-residential school or other educational establishment, (iii) a place of public worship (iv) a public house, restaurant or similar premises used for the sale to members of the public of food or drink for consumption on the premises. (v) a sports pavilion, stadium, grandstand, or other spectator accommodation. (vi) a terminus, station or other facility for air, rail, road or sea travel.
Industrial [3]	6	Factories and other premises used for manufacturing, altering, repairing, cleaning, washing, breaking-up, adapting or processing any article, generating power or slaughtering livestock.
Storage [3]	7(a)	Place for storage or deposit of goods or materials (other than described under 7(b))
	7(b)	Car parks designed to admit and accommodate only cars,
Other non-residential	8	Any other non-residential purpose not included in any other purpose group

Notes:

(1) Purpose Groups 1(a) and 1(b) include any surgery, consulting rooms, office or other accommodation not exceeding 50 m^2 in total, forming part of a dwelling and used by the occupant of the dwelling in a professional or business capacity.

(2) A building may not be treated as a place of assembly solely because it is a building to which members of the public are occasionally admitted.

(3) Appendix E gives guidance on the assessment of risk in industrial and storage buildings. The risk category of such buildings will determine many of the fire safety provisions required.

Fire Performance of Materials and Structures

0.3.3 Many of the provisions throughout this publication are given in terms of performance in relation to standard fire test methods. Details are drawn together in Appendix A and reference is made where appropriate in Sections B1 to B5.

Fire Doors

0.3.4 Provisions in respect of fire doors are set out in Appendix B. Fire doors play a significant part in the fire safety of a building. It is important to note that a fire door refers to a complete door assembly and not the door leaf alone. This point is further emphasised in sub-section 1.4 and in Appendix B.

Methods of measurement

0.3.5 Some form of measurement is an integral part of many of the provisions in this publication, and methods of measurement are set out in Appendix C (except for those methods particular to B1 set out in par. 1.0.10 to that Part).

Definitions

0.3.6 Whilst definitions that are only relevant to one of the sections in this publication are given in that section, there are other defined terms that are relevant to more than one section. These are defined in Appendix D, and for convenience that Appendix lists terms that are also defined elsewhere.

Assessment of Risk in Industrial and Storage buildings

0.3.7 The purpose groups set out in Table 0.1 can encompass a broad range of activity within an individual group. This range may affect the determination of appropriate safety requirements.

Appendix E sets out guidelines for assessment of risk in Industrial and Storage buildings (Purpose Group 6 and 7(a) respectively).

Fire Safety objectives

0.3.8 As outlined in the introduction to this Document, Building Regulations are made for specific purposes. Part B of the Second Schedule to the Building Regulations is therefore primarily concerned with the health, safety and welfare of persons. The fire safety measures outlined in this guidance document are intended for the protection of life from fire.

Reference Standards and Publications

0.3.9 For convenience, standards and other references in this Document are listed in Appendices F and G respectively.

Section B1
Means of Escape in case of Fire

Means of escape in case of fire.	**B1**	A building shall be so designed and constructed that there are adequate means of escape in case of fire from the building to a place of safety outside the building, capable of being safely and effectively used.

Performance

The requirement of B1 may be met:

(a) if there are routes of sufficient number and size, which are suitably located, to enable persons to escape to a place of safety in the event of fire;

(b) if the routes are sufficiently protected from the effects of fire in terms of enclosure, where necessary, and in the use of materials on the routes; and

(c) if sufficient lighting, means of smoke control and an alarm system to warn the occupants of the existence of fire are provided to enable them to use the routes safely;

all to an extent necessary that is dependent on the use of the building, its size and height.

Contents

1.0 Introduction to Provisions

General

1.0.1 The provisions in this Section (B1) are concerned with the measures necessary to ensure reasonable facilities for means of escape in case of fire and with structural fire precautions only where these are necessary to safeguard escape routes. They assume that the occupants of buildings will include a normal proportion of disabled people and that, in the design of the building, reliance should not be placed on external rescue by the fire brigade. The Document, therefore, has been prepared on the basis that the occupants of any part of a building should be able to escape safely from a building in an emergency without external assistance. Where it is proposed to use an alternative approach to that outlined in this Document, Codes of Practice which rely on external rescue by fire brigades are not acceptable. Special considerations, however, apply to Residential (Institutional) buildings (see pars. 1.0.6 and 1.2.7).

Attention is drawn to the fact that other legislation may impose requirements for means of escape in case of fire with which the building must comply, and which operate when the building is in use. The main legislation in this area are the Fire Services Act, 1981 and the Safety, Health and Welfare at Work Act, 1989.

Analysis of the problem

1.0.2 The design of means of escape from a building must be based on an appreciation of the probable behaviour of fire, which may break out in any part of the building and then spread to other parts. The overall design of a building should therefore be carefully analysed part by part to determine the danger which might arise from a fire, either in the part where fire may originate or in any other part of the building to which it may spread.

Fires do not normally start in two different places in a building at the same time, and initially a fire will create a hazard only in the part in which it starts and is unlikely at this stage to involve a large area. Subsequently it may spread to other parts, usually along the circulation routes of the building. Furnishings, equipment, services and plant are among the usual sources of origin. It is less likely that the fire will originate in the structure of the building itself and the risk of it originating in circulation areas, such as passages, corridors, lobbies or stairways, bearing in mind the limited combustible contents of such areas, where these are adequately restricted.

The primary danger associated with fire in its early stages is not flame but the smoke and noxious gases produced by the fire. Most of the casualties in fires have been caused by smoke, which has often also obscured the way to escape routes and exits. Measures designed to provide safe means of escape must, therefore, include provisions to limit the spread of smoke and fumes.

Criteria for Means of Escape

1.0.3 The basic principles for the design of means of escape are:

(a) there should be alternative means of escape wherever possible;

(b) where direct escape to a place of safety is not possible, the means of escape should consist of two parts -

- an unprotected escape route which should be limited in extent and should lead to a protected escape route, and

- the protected escape route which should lead to a place of safety.

The ultimate place of safety is, of course, the open air clear of the effects of the fire. In modern large and complex buildings, however, reasonable safety may be reached within the building, provided planning and protection measures are incorporated in accordance with the guidance given in this document.

The following are not acceptable as a means of escape:

(a) lifts (except a lift which is suitably designed, and installed for the purpose of evacuation);

(b) passenger conveyors or escalators;

(c) portable ladders and throw-out ladders; and

(d) manipulative apparatus and appliances.

Alternative Means of Escape

1.0.4 There is always the possibility of the path of a single escape route being rendered impassable by fire or a concentration of heavy smoke or fumes and, ideally, people should be able to turn their backs on a fire wherever it occurs and travel away from it to a protected escape route leading to a place of safety. When account is taken, however, of the way the building is to be used, there are many circumstances in which it is not reasonably possible to provide alternative means of escape from all parts of the floor or building. In limited conditions a dead-end can be accepted as providing reasonable safety. These conditions depend on the use of the building and its inherent fire risk, the size and height of the building and the numbers of persons accommodated within the dead-end.

Unprotected and Protected Escape Routes

1.0.5 The unprotected part of an escape route is that part which a person has to traverse before reaching either the safety of a final exit or the comparative safety of a protected escape route. Unprotected escape routes, therefore, should be limited in extent so that people do not have to travel excessive distances exposed to the immediate danger of fire and smoke. Even with protected horizontal escape routes the distance to a final exit or protected stairway needs to be limited because protection is not given indefinitely and the possibility of premature failure exists.

Protected stairways are designed to provide virtually "fire sterile" areas which lead to places of safety outside the building. Once inside a protected stairway, a person can be considered to be safe from immediate danger from flame and smoke and can then proceed to a place of safety at his or her own pace. To enable this to be done, flames, smoke and other products of combustion must be excluded from these escape routes (as far as is possible) by fire and smoke resisting structures or by an appropriate smoke control system, or a combination of both these methods. This does not preclude the use of unprotected stairways for day-to-day circulation, but these "accommodation" stairways can only play a very limited role in terms of means of escape.

Progressive Horizontal Escape in Hospitals and Similar Buildings

1.0.6 In areas designed for patients in hospitals and similar buildings the principle of total evacuation of a building in the event of fire may be initially inappropriate.

Able-bodied staff employed for the care and supervision of people in hospitals are normally available and trained to assist them in escaping from the immediate danger of fire, although the ratio of staff to disabled occupants can vary considerably. It is, therefore, appropriate to adopt the principle of progressive, staged evacuation of occupants from an area in which fire occurs to an adjoining area (or areas) on the same level which affords sufficient protection from the fire and smoke to enable them (and the occupants of the adjoining area) to remain safe until the fire has been dealt with. Progressive horizontal escape should always be planned to ensure that, if further stages of evacuation become necessary, ultimately a protected vertical escape route is reached. A whole floor would be evacuated by means of a stairway (or a suitably protected bed/evacuation lift) only as a last resort if the fire could not be brought under control. The principle could be of value to adopt in any Residential (Institutional) building (Purpose Groups 2(a)).

Security

1.0.7 There is potential for conflict between the need for easy and rapid evacuation of a building in case of fire, and the control of entry and exit in the interest of security. Measures to prevent unauthorised access can also hinder fire service entry to rescue people trapped by fire. It is important that any potential conflicts are identified and resolved at the design stage and not left to ad-hoc expedients after completion.

Use of the Document

1.0.8 Guidance with regard to the provision of

means of escape are outlined in 1.1 to 1.5 of this Section (B1).

Sub-section 1.1 indicates where the appropriate guidance on means of escape may be obtained. It refers to codes of practice and other documents for different purpose groups and building types, which should be used where applicable, and to other sub-sections of this technical guidance document, where appropriate.

Sub-sections 1.2 and 1.3 set out the provisions for means of escape for buildings other than those where reference is made in 1.1 to codes of practice or other documents. For these buildings, guidance on the provision of means of escape is subdivided into the following components:

- horizontal escape routes (1.2) and

- vertical escape routes (1.3)

Sub-section 1.4 sets out provisions in respect of the construction and protection of escape routes generally and applies to all buildings except dwelling houses. The provisions of 1.4 take precedence over provisions of a similar nature contained in any codes of practice or other documents referred to in 1.1.

Sub-section 1.5 sets out provisions for means of escape in dwelling houses, including provisions in the case of conversion of lofts in houses to habitable accommodation.

Many of the codes of practice and other documents referred to in 1.1 make references to statutory provisions which may not be applicable. These documents are quoted solely for the purpose of providing appropriate technical guidance to meet the requirements of the Building Regulations.

Definitions

1.0.9 The following definitions apply specifically to B1. Other terms applicable more widely throughout this Technical Guidance Document are given in Appendix D.

Access room - Room through which passes the only escape route from an inner room.

Access level - A level used for normal access to a building that either incorporates, or leads directly to, a place of safety.

Accommodation stairway - A stairway additional to that or those required for escape purposes, provided for the convenience of occupants.

Alternative escape routes - Escape routes sufficiently separated by either direction and space, or by fire-resisting construction, to ensure that one is still available should the other be affected by fire.

Atrium (plural atria) - a vertical space within a building (other than a shaft used solely for stairways, lifts or services), openly connecting three or more storeys in a building and enclosed at the top by a floor or roof.

Bedroom - A room within a dwelling, Residential (Institutional) or Other Residential building which is used as sleeping accommodation.

Dead-end - Area from which escape is possible in one direction only.

Direct distance - The shortest distance from any point within the floor area, measured within the external enclosures of the building, to the nearest storey exit, ignoring walls, partitions and fittings, other than the enclosing walls/partitions to protected stairways ($^2/_3$rd permitted travel distance can be used for design purposes).

Emergency lighting - Lighting provided for use when the power supply to the normal lighting fails.

Escape lighting - That part of the emergency lighting which is provided to ensure that the escape route is illuminated at all material times.

Escape route - A route by which a person may reach a place of safety, and, in relation to any point in a building, a route from that point to a place of safety.

Evacuation lift - A lift that may be used for the evacuation of disabled people in a fire.

Final exit - The termination of an escape route from a building giving direct access to a street, passageway, walkway or open space, and sited to ensure the rapid dispersal of persons from the vicinity of a building so that they are no longer in danger from fire and/or smoke.

Habitable room - A room used for living or sleeping purposes but does not include a kitchen having a floor area less than 6.5 m^2, a bathroom or toilet.

Inner room - A room from which escape is possible only by passing through an access room.

Means of escape - Physical means whereby a safe route or routes is or are provided for persons to travel from any point in a building to a place of safety.

Open spatial planning - The internal arrangement of a building in which more than one storey or level is contained in one undivided volume e.g. split-level floors and balconies or gallery floors overlooking an unenclosed atrium (but not atrium galleries used only for circulation).

Place of Safety - A place, normally in the open air at ground level, in which persons are in no danger from fire.

Places of special fire risk - Transformer and switchgear rooms, large commercial kitchens, boiler rooms, fuel or other highly flammable substance storage spaces, rooms housing a fixed internal combustion engine and areas where flammable vapours are likely to be present in the atmosphere. Note: Places of special fire risk may also be identified in codes of practice or other documents referred to in 1.1 in relation to particular building uses.

Pressurization - A method of protecting escape routes against the ingress of smoke by maintaining an air pressure difference between the route and adjoining accommodation.

Protected corridor/lobby - A corridor or lobby which is adequately protected from fire in adjoining accommodation by fire-resisting construction.

Protected stairway - A stairway which is adequately protected from fire in the accommodation through which it passes by fire-resisting construction and discharges through a final exit to a place of safety.

Storey - means any of the parts into which a building is divided horizontally above or below ground level but excluding any part of a building situated above the level of the roof or in the roofspace, or below the level of the lowest floor, which is intended for the protection of a water tank, or lift motor room, or similar use and is not intended for, or adapted to be used for habitable purposes, or as a work room, or as a store room.

For the purpose of B1 a storey also includes:

(a) any gallery in an assembly and recreation building; and

(b) any gallery in any other building if its area exceeds half of the space into which it projects.

Storey exit - A final exit, or a doorway opening into a protected stairway, firefighting lobby or external escape route, or a doorway in a compartment wall that is common to two or more buildings (a separating wall).

Travel distance - (unless otherwise specified) The actual distance to be travelled by a person from any point within the floor area to the nearest storey exit, having regard to the layout of walls, partitions and fittings.

Methods of Measurement

1.0.10 The following methods of measurement apply specifically to B1. Other methods of measurement applicable more widely throughout this Document are given in the definitions in Appendix D, and illustrated in Appendix C.

(a) Occupant capacity of a:

  (i) room or storey - is the maximum number of persons it is designed to hold (where this is known) or the number calculated (using the occupancy load factors given in Table 1.1) from -

area of room or storey (m²)
occupancy load factor

Note: 'area' excludes stairway enclosures, lifts and sanitary accommodation.

(ii) building or part of a building - is the sum of the number of occupants of the storeys in the building or part.

(b) Travel distance - is by way of the shortest route, which if:

(i) there is fixed seating or other fixed obstructions, is along the centre line of the seatways and gangways;

(ii) it includes a stairway, is along the pitch line on the centre line of travel.

(c) Width of a:

(i) Doorway - is the width of the opening door leaf (or the sum of the widths of both opening door leaves in the case of double doors);

Note: It is assumed that the door leaf is free to open to an angle of at least 90° .

(ii) Escape route - is the width at shoulder level when defined by walls (handrails fixed to walls may be ignored) or, elsewhere, the minimum width of passage available between any fixed obstructions; and

(iii) Stairway - is the clear width between the walls or balustrades, (strings and handrails intruding not more than 30 mm and 100 mm respectively may be ignored).

Application to Existing Building

1.0.11 The following paragraphs relate to the application of the means of escape provisions of the Building Regulations to existing buildings.

1.0.11.1 Alternative documents - The requirements in relation to means of escape in case of fire may be met by the use of any appropriate guidance document, code of practice or standard, other than those referred to in 1.1, provided the level of fire safety achieved is adequate to meet the requirements of the Building Regulations. Where alternative guidance is used, consideration should be given to links between the means of escape provisions and those appropriate to other fire safety requirements of the Regulations (see 0.1.2).

Table 1.1 **Occupancy load factor**

	Accommodation (1)	Occupancy load factor
1.	Standing area in assembly and recreation building	0.3
2.	Bar, lounge bar	0.5
3.	Restaurant, dining room, meeting room, committee room, staff room	1.0(2)
4.	Factory production area, open plan offices	5.0
5.	Bedroom or study bedroom	8.0(3)
6.	Offices, kitchen	7.0
7.	Storage building, car park	30.0(4)

Notes:

(1) Includes categories appropriate to those purpose groups and building types other than those covered by codes of practice and other documents outlined in pars. 1.1.1 to 1.1.6.

Where accommodation is not directly covered by the descriptions given, the nearest reasonable value may be selected.

(2) Alternatively the occupant capacity may be taken as the number of seats provided, if the occupants will normally be seated. In the case of continuous seating, a width of 400 mm should be allowed per person.

(3) Alternatively the number of bed spaces provided.

(4) Alternatively 2 persons per parking space.

1.0.11.2 Alternative solutions - Where it is impracticable to comply fully with a particular requirement of this Technical Guidance Document, it may be necessary to consider alternative solutions which best fit the particular circumstances (see also 0.1.4 and 0.1.5). The provision of compensating fire safety measures may also be necessary and these could include a range of passive and/or active measures.

1.0.11.3 Compensating measures - Where compensating fire safety measures for the purposes of means of escape are provided, the nature and extent of such provisions will depend on the circumstances in each particular case. However such measures are likely to include some or all of the following:

- Enhanced levels of life safety protection by automatic fire detection and alarm systems;
- Reduced travel distances;
- Enhanced smoke control measures;
- Pressurisation of stairway enclosures;
- Protection to escape routes from places of special fire risk;
- Enhanced performance of fire doors;
- Additional structural fire protection measures, such as increased levels of compartmentation of the building (see Section B3).

This list is not exhaustive or in any order of preference and is indicative of the range of options that may be considered.

1.0.11.4 Material alterations - Where works constitute a material alteration, and where a material change of use of the building is not also involved, the means of escape requirements of the building regulations for the material alteration may be met by the application of means of escape provisions, together with any other provisions in relation to the protection of escape routes, emergency lighting, fire detection and alarms, fire suppression and building services contained in:

- Any relevant Guide or Code of Practice, published by the Department of the Environment for the purpose of providing guidance in relation to satisfying obligations under section 18(2) of the Fire Services Act, 1981.

An example of this type of guidance document is "Fire Safety in Flats, A Guide to Fire Safety in Flats, Bedsitters and Apartments" (July, 1994).

Provisions meeting the Requirement

1.1 Means of Escape Provisions for Different Purpose Groups and Building Types

Purpose Groups 1(a) and 1(b)
Dwelling Houses

1.1.1 Guidance on means of escape in dwelling houses, Purpose Group 1(a) and 1(b), including provisions for conversion of lofts in houses to habitable accommodation, is provided in:

- Sub-section 1.5 (dwelling houses) of this Technical Guidance Document.

Purpose Group 1(c)
Flats and Maisonettes

1.1.2 Guidance on the provision of means of escape in buildings containing flats and maisonettes, etc. Residential (Dwellings), Purpose Group 1(c), is provided in the following:

- BS 5588: Part 1: 1990, Fire precautions in the design, construction and use of buildings, Part 1, Code of practice for residential buildings;

  and

- Sub-section 1.4 (general provisions for means of escape) of this Technical Guidance Document.

Section three of BS 5588: Part 1 contains recommendations in relation to the internal planning of flats and maisonettes, escape routes from dwellings with corridor, lobby or open balcony approach and vertical escape routes by way of common stairways. Recommendations are also included for stairways in buildings which contain dwellings and other uses (mixed user buildings).

Section five of BS 5588: Part 1 contains recommendations in relation to accommodation ancillary to flats and maisonettes.

Purpose Group 2(a) (Part)
Hospitals

1.1.3 Guidance on the provision of means of escape in hospitals is provided in the following:

- Firecode Health Technical Memorandum 81, Fire precautions in new hospitals, 1996 (HTM 81: 1996)

Hospitals, in particular, require that evacuation procedures be given special consideration in the design of the means of escape. The principle of progressive horizontal evacuation is particularly relevant. Guidance on progressive horizontal evacuation and the provision of compartmentation for this purpose is contained in Chapters 3 and 5 of HTM 81: 1996. Compartmentation is also required for the purpose of satisfying the requirements of regulation B3 - Internal fire spread (structure) and guidance on this is contained in 3.2 of this Technical Guidance Document.

Purpose Group 3
Offices

1.1.4 Guidance on the provision of means of escape in offices is provided in the following:

- BS 5588: Part 11 : 1997, Fire precautions in the design, construction and use of buildings, Part 11. Code of practice for shops, offices, industrial, storage and other similar buildings; and

- Sub-section 1.4 (General Provisions for means of escape) of this Technical Guidance Document.

Section 3 of BS 5588: Part 11 contains recommendations in relation to the provision of escape routes from offices. Section 5 contains recommendations on means of escape for ancillary accommodation.

Where offices form part of a shopping complex, additional recommendations for this situation are contained in BS 5588: Part 10, Fire precautions in the design, construction and use of buildings, Part 10. Code of practice for shopping complexes.

Purpose Group 4(a) and 4(b)
Shops and Shopping Centres

1.1.5 Guidance on the provision of means of escape in shops and shopping centres is provided in the following:

- BS 5588: Part 11: 1997, Fire precautions in the design, construction and use of buildings, Part 11. Code of practice for shops, offices, industrial, storage and other similar buildings; and

- Section 1.4 (General Provisions for means of escape) of this Technical Guidance Document; and where appropriate

- BS 5588: Part 10, Fire precautions in the design, construction and use of buildings, Part 10, Code of practice for shopping complexes.

Section 3 of BS 5588: Part 11 contains recommendations in relation to the provision of escape routes from shops. Section 5 contains recommendations on means of escape for ancillary accommodation.

Section 4 of BS 5588: Part 10 contains recommendations in relation to means of escape in shopping complexes. BS 5588: Part 10 also contains relevant supplementary guidance on means of escape for other uses, where these form part of a shopping centre.

Although the guidance in BS 5588: Part 11 is also relevant to individual shops which are part of a shopping centre, additional recommendations for these situations are contained in BS 5588: Part 10. The recommendations in Chapter 10 of BS 5588: Part 11 in relation to small premises do not apply when they are part of a shopping complex.

Note: Cafes, restaurants, public houses and other places of refreshments are regarded as Places of Assembly (Purpose Group 5) for the purpose of the Building Regulations and this Technical Guidance Document.

Purpose Group 5
Assembly and Recreation

1.1.6 Assembly and Recreation use includes a wide range of building types. Accordingly the relevant guidance will vary according to the sub-division, by building type, outlined below:

(i) Assembly and recreation buildings other than those used as a public house, restaurant, or similar premises, sports pavilion, stadium, grandstand or other spectator accommodation or school:

Appropriate guidance is contained in the following:

- BS 5588: Part 6: 1991, Fire precautions in the design, construction and use of buildings, Part 6, Code of practice for places of assembly; and

- Sub-section 1.4 (general provisions for means of escape) of this Technical Guidance Document.

(ii) Sports pavilion, stadium, grandstand or other spectator accommodation:

Appropriate guidance is contained in the following:

- Code of Practice for Safety at Sports Grounds, published by the Department of Education.

In this type of building, where assembly and recreation areas, other than spectator accommodation, are also provided (such as a bar or restaurant), the relevant guidance outlined at (iv) below should be used.

(iii) Guidance on the provision of means of escape in schools is provided in the following:

- Department of Education and Science (UK) Building Bulletin 7, Fire and the design of educational buildings; and

- Sub-section 1.4 (general provisions for means of escape) of this technical guidance document.

Recommendations in relation to means of escape are contained in paragraphs 34 to 91 inclusive of Building Bulletin 7.

Buildings or parts of buildings which form part of a school or other educational facility may be used for purposes which are outside the scope of Building Bulletin 7. Where these occur, they should comply with the relevant code of practice or other document outlined in this sub-section (1.1).

(iv) Buildings used as a public house, restaurant or similar premises and buildings other than indicated in (i), (ii) and (iii) above.

Appropriate guidance is contained in sub-sections 1.2 to 1.4 of this Technical Guidance Document.

Where another use forms part (other than where ancillary) of an assembly and recreation building, the appropriate guidance in this section should be used. Where a place of assembly forms part of a shopping centre, additional recommendations for these situations are contained in BS 5588: Part 10.

Other Purpose Groups
Other Building Types

1.1.7 Guidance on means of escape for buildings other than those indicated in 1.1.1 to 1.1.6 above is provided in the following sections of this Technical Guidance Document:

- Sub-section 1.2: Design for horizontal escape;

- Sub-section 1.3: Design for vertical escape; and

- Sub-section 1.4: General provisions for means of escape.

1.2 Design for Horizontal Escape

Introduction

1.2.1 The general principle to be followed when designing facilities for means of escape is that any person confronted by an outbreak of fire within a building can turn away from it and make a safe escape. This sub-section deals with the provision of means of escape from any point to the storey exit of the floor in question, for all types of building other than those covered by codes of practice or other documents which are referred to in sub-section 1.1.

This sub-section should be read in conjunction with the general provisions for means of escape in sub-section 1.4.

Number of Escape Routes and Exits

1.2.2 The number of escape routes and exits to be provided from a room or storey depends on the following factors:

- the number of occupants (see 1.2.2.1);

- the limitations on travel distance (see 1.2.2.2 and Table 1.2); and

- the minimum number of escape routes required (see 1.2.2.4 and Table 1.3);

1.2.2.1 Number of occupants - The figure used for the number of occupants will normally be the design figure. When the number of occupants likely to use a room or storey is not known, the appropriate capacity should be calculated on the basis of the occupant capacity. Guidance is set out in paragraph 1.0.10 of this Document and Table 1.1. There may be cases where it may be reasonable to depart from the stated occupancy load factors.

The number of occupants in a room or storey will determine the width of escape routes and exits to be provided (see 1.2.4). The widths required to provide sufficient occupant capacity will also influence the number of escape routes and exits that are required.

1.2.2.2 Travel distance - The travel distance (see 1.0.9 for definition) from any point in a room or storey should not exceed the appropriate values indicated in Table 1.2 (illustrated in Diagram 1). The permitted travel distance will depend on whether escape is available in one direction only or in more than one direction. Escape is available in more than one direction where alternative escape routes exist (see 1.2.2.3).

Note: Travel distance limitations for Purpose Groups other than those indicated in Table 1.2 are contained in the appropriate code of practice or other document referred to in sub-section 1.1.

1.2.2.3 Alternative escape routes - A choice of escape routes is of little value if they are all likely to be disabled simultaneously. Every escape route from a storey should be independent of any other escape route to which access may be obtained directly from that storey.

Alternative escape routes should satisfy the following criteria:

(a) they are in directions 45° or more apart (Diagram 2 (a)); or

(b) they are in directions less than 45° apart, but are separated from each other by fire-resisting construction (Diagram 2 (b)); or

(c) (from any point from which there is initially a single direction of escape) they are in directions apart equal to 45° plus 2.5° for every metre travelled in one direction (Diagram 2 (c)).

Diagram 1 **Travel distances** *Par. 1.2.2.2*

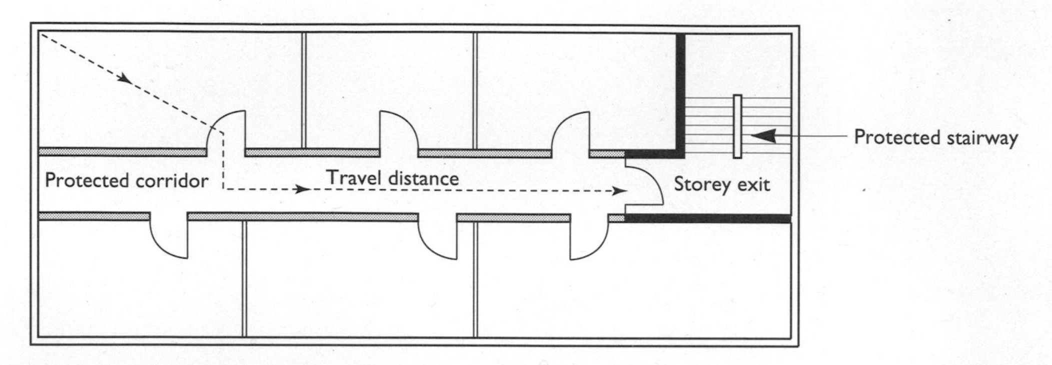

1. ESCAPE IN ONE DIRECTION ONLY (CORRIDOR)

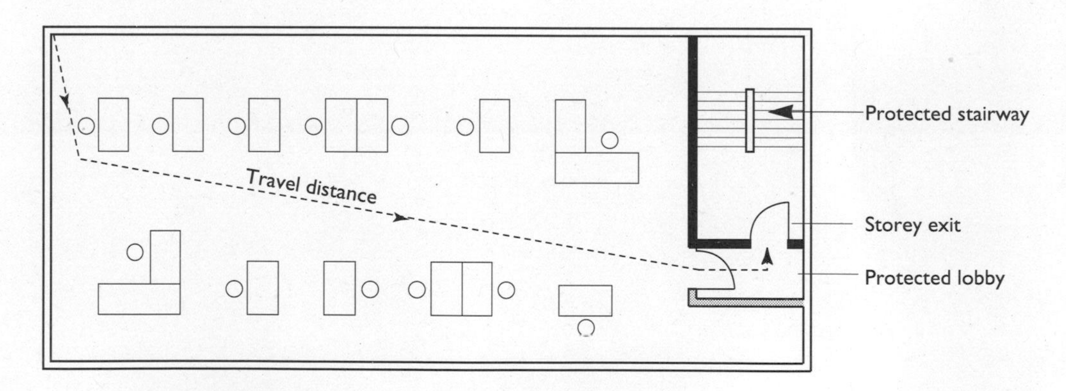

2. ESCAPE IN ONE DIRECTION ONLY (OPEN PLAN)

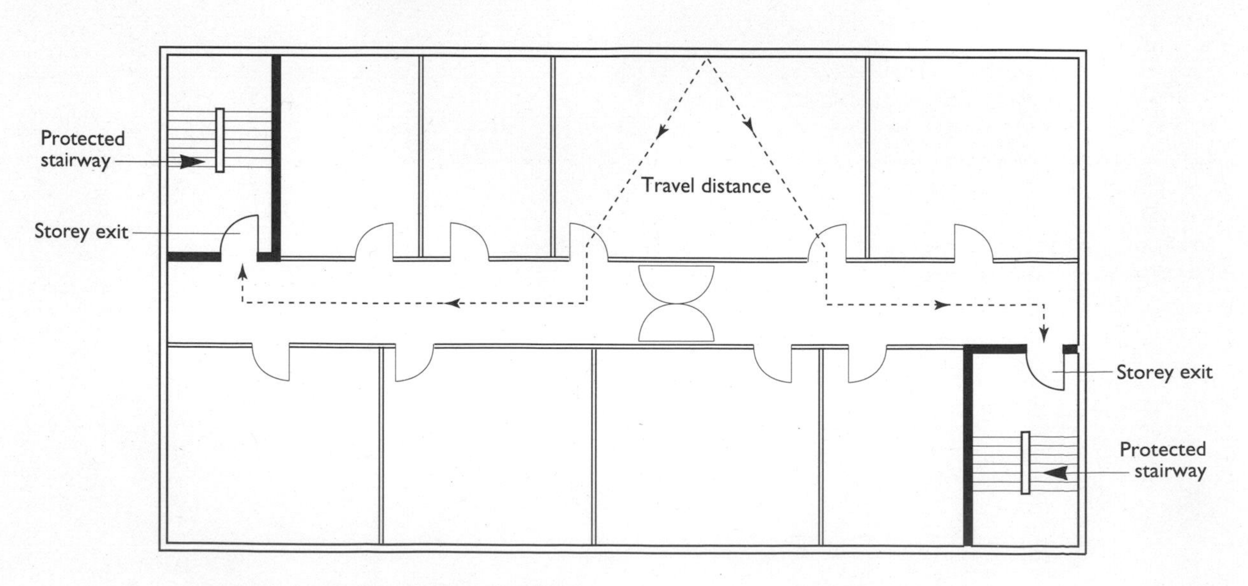

3. ESCAPE IN MORE THAN ONE DIRECTION

Table 1.2 **Limitations on Travel Distance**

Purpose Group(s) [1]	Use of premises or part of premises	Maximum travel distance[2] related to available direction of escape	
		In one direction	In more than one direction
2(a)	Residential (Institutional)	10	20
2(b)	Other Residential:		
	(a) bedroom [3]	10	20
	(b) bedroom corridor	10	35
	(c) elsewhere	20	35
5	Assembly and recreation		
	(a) areas with seating in rows	15	32
	(b) other areas	18	45
	(c) buildings primarily for use by disabled persons	9	18
6	Industrial[4]		
	(a) normal risk	25	45
	(b) high risk	12	25
7(a)	Storage[4]		
	(a) normal risk	18	45
	(b) high risk	15	32
7(b)	Car Parks	18	45
8	Other Non-Residential	18	45
2 - 8	Places of special fire risk [5]	9	18
2 - 8	Plant-room or roof-top plant		
	(a) within room[3]	9	35
	(b) total travel (enclosed)	18	45
	(c) total travel (open air)	60	100

Notes:

(1) Purpose Groups are defined in Table 0.1 to Section B0.

(2) Where the internal arrangement of walls and fixed furniture is not known, direct distance may be used for assessment. For design purposes, the direct distance may be taken as 2/3rds. of the travel distance. However, the final layout should not create travel distances which exceed the tabulated values.

(3) Denotes the maximum part of total travel which is within a room.

(4) See Appendix E for assessment of risk in industrial and storage buildings.

(5) Places of special fire risk are defined in par. 1.0.9.

Diagram 2 Alternative escape routes *Par. 1.2.2.3*

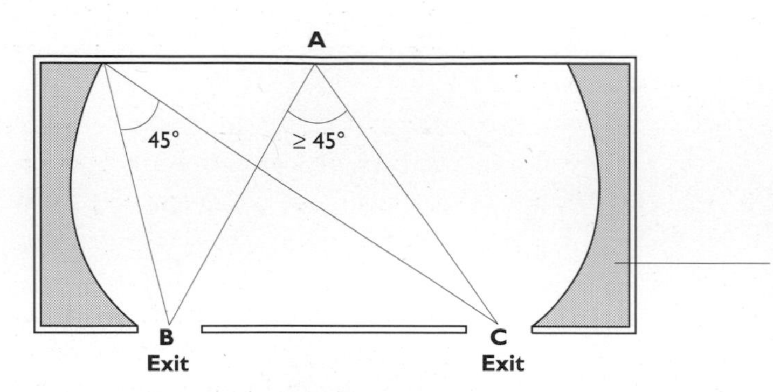

Two directions of escape assumed if angle indicated is 45° or more.

In hatched areas where the angle will be less than 45° at any point, one direction of escape only should be assumed and dead end conditions will apply.

(a) IN DIRECTIONS 45° OR MORE APART

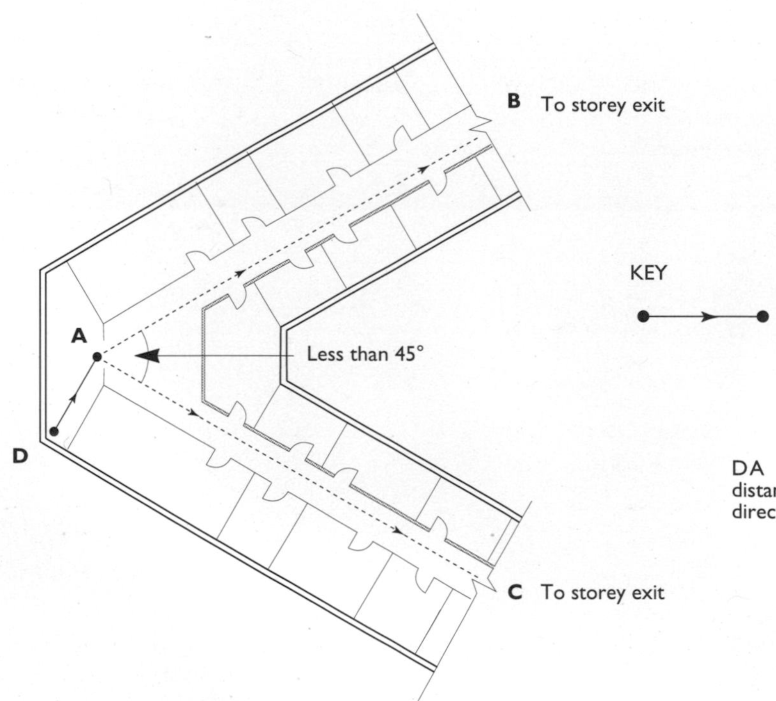

KEY

Dead end condition

DA not to exceed distance allowed for single direction of travel.

(b) IN DIRECTIONS LESS THAN 45° APART

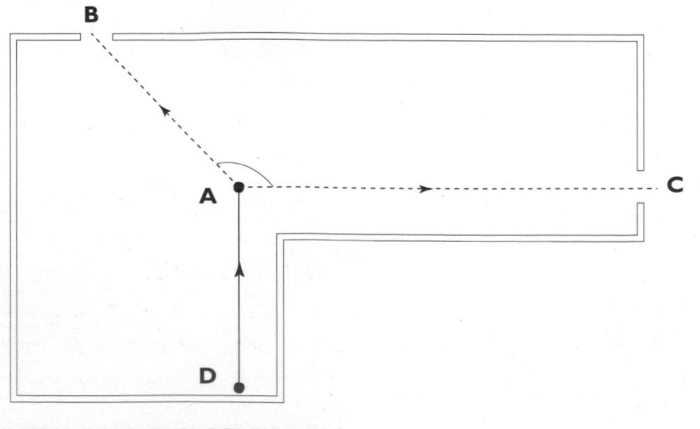

Angle BAC ≐ 45° + 2.5° for every metre travelled from D to A.

Note: DA not to exceed that allowed for single direction of travel.

Single escape route exists at D.

(c) INITIAL DEAD END CONDITION

1.2.2.4 Minimum number of escape routes - The number of escape routes from any room or storey should be not less than that indicated in Table 1.3, except where permitted by par. 1.2.2.5 to be served by a single escape route.

Table 1.3 **Minimum number of escape routes**

Number of persons accommodated	Minimum number of escape routes
1 to 500	2
More than 500	3

1.2.2.5 Single escape route - In order to avoid occupants being trapped by fire or smoke, there should be alternative escape routes from all parts of the building except for the situations listed below where a single route can be acceptable:

(a) areas, except in a building of purpose group 2(a), Residential (Institutional), not likely to contain more than 50 persons, near enough to an exit to satisfy the limits on travel in one direction indicated in Table 1.2;

(b) rooms which are not likely to contain more than 50 people, or 20 people if the building is in Residential (Institutional) use, provided that the limits on travel in one direction only are satisfied (see Table 1.2); or

(c) a storey, except in the case of a building of purpose group 2(a), Residential (Institutional), which is not likely to contain more than 50 people, where the limits on travel in one direction only are satisfied (see Table 1.2).

In many cases the beginning of the escape route will be in one direction only (i.e. a single escape route) to a point where there are alternative escape routes. This is acceptable provided that the total travel distance to the nearest exit is within the limits for routes where escape is possible in more than one direction and the section with the single escape route does not exceed the limit for escape in one direction only (see Table 1.2 and Diagram 2(c)).

Planning of Escape Routes and Exits

1.2.3 The basic principle of escape route planning is that unless a route is very short, there should be an alternative which will not be affected if fire or smoke makes the first route impassable.

Every escape route should lead to a place of safety, and should give direct access to that place of safety, or give access thereto only by means of a circulation area.

1.2.3.1 Inner rooms - A room whose only escape route is through another room is at risk if a fire starts in that other room. It is termed an inner room and is at risk from a fire in the outer room (access room).

Such an arrangement is only acceptable if the following conditions are satisfied:

(a) the inner room should not be likely to have more than 20 occupants;

(b) the inner room should not be a bedroom;

(c) the escape route from the inner room should not pass through more than one outer (access) room;

(d) the travel distance from any point in the inner room to the exit(s) from the access room should not exceed the appropriate limit given in Table 1.2;

(e) the access room should not be a place of special fire risk and it should be in the control of the same occupier; and

(f) one of the following arrangements are made -

(i) the enclosures (walls or partitions) of the inner room are stopped at least 500 mm below the ceiling, or

(ii) a vision panel is located in the enclosure of the inner room, of sufficient size, to enable occupants of the inner room to see if a fire has started in the outer room, or

(iii) the access room is fitted with a suitable

fire detection and alarm system to warn the occupants of the inner room should an outbreak of fire occur in the access room.

1.2.3.2 Open connections between floors - Routes and exits should not be prejudiced by open connections between floors. Where travel is in one direction only, it should not be within 5 m of an open connection between floors unless it is leading away from the opening. Where there is a choice of routes, at least one of them should lead away from the opening (see Diagram 3).

1.2.3.3 Planning of exits in a central core - Buildings with more than one exit in a central core should be planned so that storey exits are remote from one another, and so that no two exits are approached from the same lift hall, common lobby or undivided corridor, or linked by any of these (see Diagram 4).

1.2.3.4 Access to storey exits - A storey which should have more than one escape stairway should be planned so that it is not necessary to pass through one stairway to reach another.

1.2.3.5 Separation of circulation routes from stairways - An escape stairway should not form part of the primary circulation route between different parts of the building at the same level. An exception to this requirement may be made in the case of a building, having not more than three storeys (see Appendix C, Diagram 36), which is served by a single escape stairway (see 1.3.3) where rooms open directly into the enclosure to the stairway and where self-closing fire doors are unlikely to be rendered ineffective as a result of constant use.

Diagram 3 **Exit routes in relation to openings between floors** *Par. 1.2.3.2*

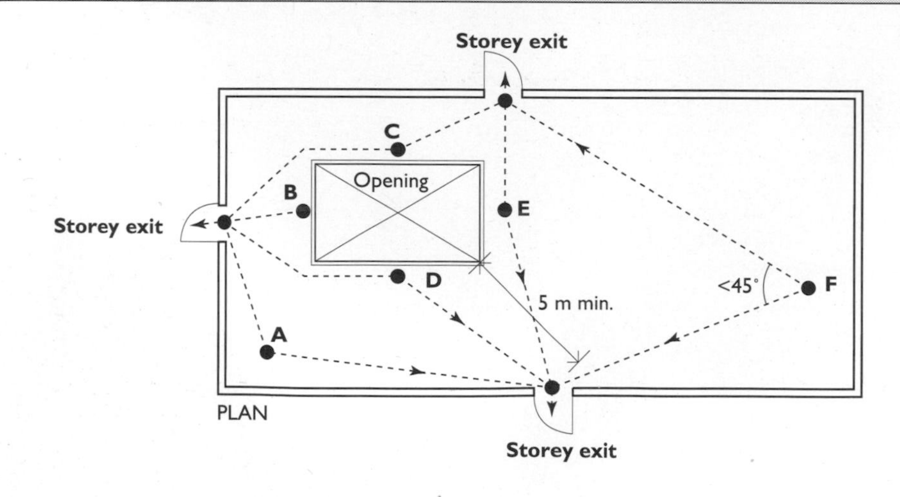

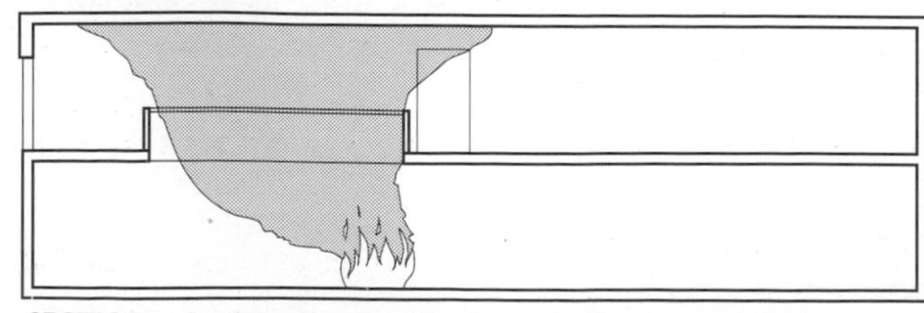

SECTION - (with smoke spreading between floors via opening)

NOTES

1. Where the exit route is not away from the opening there should be a choice of routes, as at A, C or F.
2. Point F does not have alternative escape routes. Single escape route should not be less than 5 m from any open connection between floors.
3. Routes should not all lead towards an opening.

Diagram 4 **Central core arrangement** *Par. 1.2.3.3*

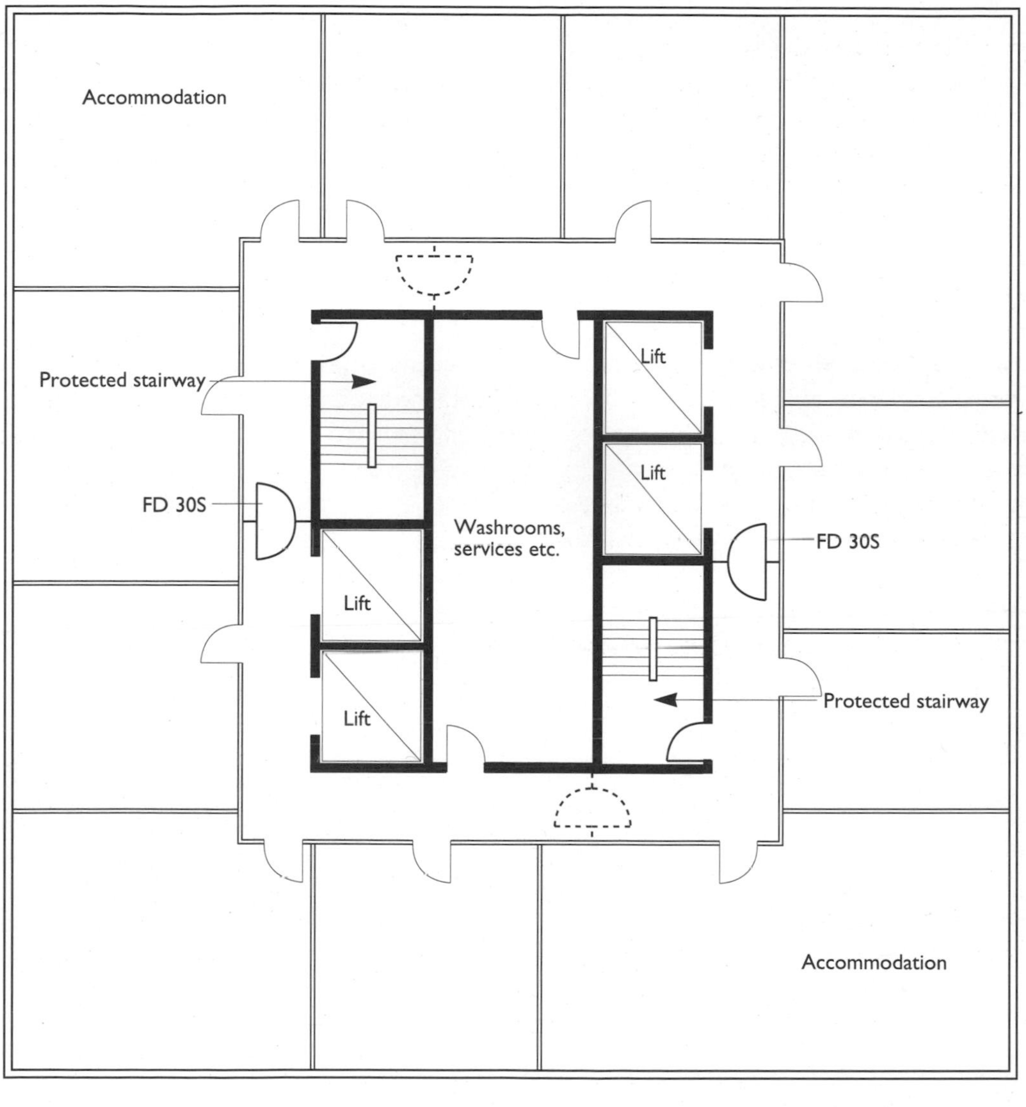

Accommodation

Protected stairway

FD 30S

Lift

Lift

Washrooms, services etc.

Lift

Lift

FD 30S

Protected stairway

Accommodation

NOTE: Possible alternative position of fire doors shown dotted.

1.2.3.6 Storeys divided into different occupancies - Where any storey is divided into separate occupancies (i.e. where there are separate ownerships or tenancies of different organisations):

(a) the means of escape from each occupancy should in general not pass through any other occupancy;

(b) the common corridor serving the different occupancies should be a protected corridor (see 1.2.5.1); and

(c) a fire detection and alarm system, complying with the requirements for at least an L3 type system as defined in IS 3218: 1989, should be provided throughout the storey (see 1.4.14).

Width of Escape Routes and Exits

1.2.4 The width of escape routes and exits depends on the number of persons needing to use them, and should not be less than the dimensions given in Table 1.4.

Table 1.4 Width of escape routes and exits

Maximum number of persons	Minimum width (mm)
50	800 (1)
100	900
150	1000
220	1100
More than 220	5 per person

Note

(1) May be reduced to 530 mm for gangways between fixed storage racking in buildings of purpose group 6 or 7.

There is a possibility that one escape route may become unavailable due to a fire in a building. Except where permitted to be served by a single escape route (see 1.2.2.5), or where all the exits from an area open directly to the open air at ground floor level, it will be necessary to take account of this when calculating the total capacity of available escape routes. It is therefore necessary to consider the effect of discounting each escape route in turn.

The total capacity of the escape routes and exits from any room or storey should be adequate for the number of occupants, taking account of discounting, where required. The total capacity should be based on the sum of the capacities of each individual escape route or exit, based on the values indicated in Table 1.4, with an allowance for discounting where applicable.

In assembly and recreation buildings (purpose Group 5), the escape route provided by the main entrance to the building should be capable of discharging at least one third of the occupant capacity in accordance with the provisions of Table 1.4.

In Residential (Institutional) buildings (Purpose Group 2(a)) an escape route should generally be not less than 1150 mm in width and and where appropriate be suitably designed to allow the movement of beds along the escape route. The width of an exit from any room should be adequate for the appropriate evacuation procedures, taking into account the physical capacity and dependency of the occupants and should not be less than 900 mm.

Special provisions, which include the width of seatways and gangways, apply to areas with closely seated audiences (see 1.2.8).

1.2.5 Corridors

1.2.5.1 Protected corridors - A corridor which serves as part of the means of escape in any of the following circumstances should be a protected corridor (see Table A1, Appendix A):

(a) every corridor serving sleeping accommodation within Residential (Institutional) or other Residential buildings (Purpose Groups 2(a) or 2(b));

(b) every dead-end corridor;

(c) any corridor common to two or more different occupancies (see also par. 1.2.3.6).

1.2.5.2 Enclosure of corridors that are not protected corridors - The enclosures to all corridors used as means of escape (which are not protected corridors) should be carried up to the underside of the structural floor above (or to a suspended ceiling) and all openings in the corridor enclosures should be fitted with doors.

1.2.5.3 Sub-division of corridors - If a corridor provides access to alternative escape routes, there is a risk that smoke will spread along it and make both routes impassable before all occupants have escaped. To avoid this, every corridor connecting two or more storey exits where the distance between protected doorways exceeds 12 m should be sub-divided by self-closing fire doors (and any necessary associated screens) so that:

(a) no length of undivided corridor is common to two storey exits; and

(b) the fire door(s) are positioned to effectively safeguard the route from smoke, having regard to the layout of the corridor and to any adjacent fire risks.

1.2.5.4 Separation of dead-ends - If a dead-end portion of a corridor provides access to a point from which alternative escape routes are available,

Building Regulations, 1997

Addenda et Corrigenda

Amendment to Technical Guidance Documents (1997)

The section entitled **"Transitional Arrangements"** in Page 2 of each of the Technical Guidance Documents is amended as follows:-

4th line: Replace the "1 January, 1998" with "1 July, 1998".

11th line: Replace the "1 January, 1998" with "1 July, 1998".

---

roof, provided that:

(a) the route does not serve a Residential (Institutional) building, or a part of a building intended for use by members of the public;

(b) the roof is part of the same building from which escape is being made, or if it is part of another building, there is a legal agreement between the parties concerned which includes a right of entry into that building;

(c) the route across the roof leads to a storey exit;

(d) the part of the roof forming the escape route and its supporting structure, together with any opening within 3 m of the escape route, is fire-resisting; and

(e) the route is adequately defined and guarded by walls and/or protective barriers which meet the provisions in Technical Guidance Document K.

In the case of any existing building, an escape route by way of a flat roof which complies with (b) to (e) above may be acceptable as an alternative means of escape, where combined with an external escape stairway as outlined at 1.2.6.1 above. Where the building is used for assembly and recreation the numbers of persons likely to use such an escape route should not exceed 150.

The provisions of this paragraph do not prohibit an escape route by way of an external podium which gives direct access to a place of safety and where the roof is constructed of non-combustible construction having a fire resistance of at least 60 minutes.

Diagram 5 **Dead end corridors** *Par. 1.2.5.4*

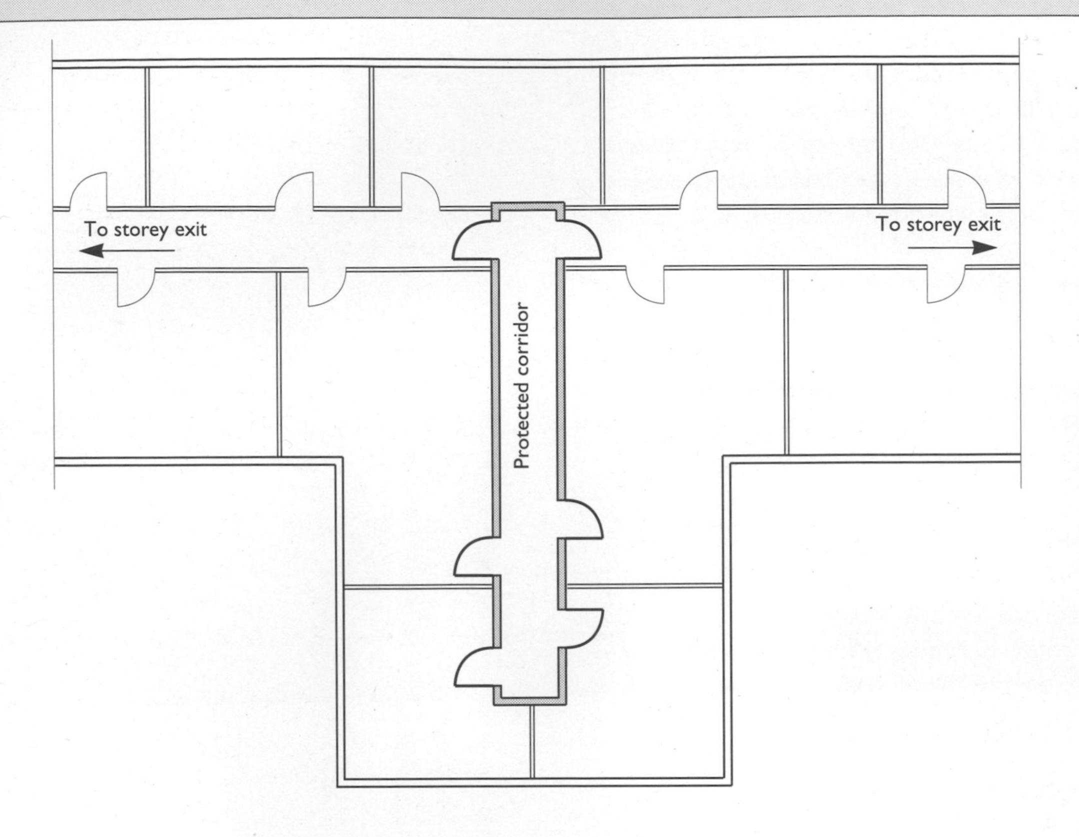

(a) T - JUNCTION WITH MAIN CORRIDOR

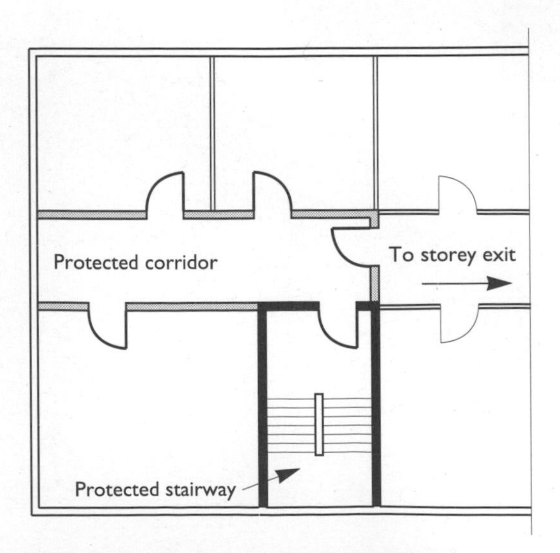

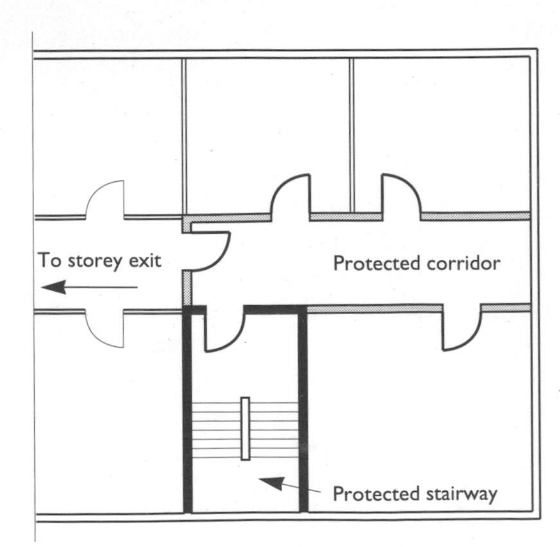

(b) CONTINUATION PAST ESCAPE STAIRWAYS

KEY

30 minutes fire resisting construction

Fire door (FD 30S)

1.2.7 Evacuation Considerations

1.2.7.1 General - In premises of Purpose Group 2(a), Residential (Institutional), occupants may be totally dependant on other people for evacuation. Normal "self-help" evacuation procedures are therefore inappropriate and consideration must be given to designing escape routes to facilitate the planned mode of evacuation. The following provisions should be made to allow progressive horizontal escape to be made into adjoining compartments in those parts of buildings used to accommodate occupants of this type. The object is to provide a place of relative safety within a short distance, from which further evacuation can be made if necessary but under less pressure of time.

1.2.7.2 Compartmentation - Every storey used for occupants of the type described in 1.2.7.1 above should be divided into at least two compartments in such a way as to permit horizontal evacuation of each compartment.

1.2.7.3 Planning for progressive horizontal evacuation - In planning a storey which is divided into compartments for progressive horizontal evacuation, the following conditions should be observed:

(a) Adjoining compartments into which horizontal evacuation may take place should each have a floor area sufficient to accommodate not only their own occupants but the occupants from the adjoining compartment. This should be calculated on the basis of the design occupancy of the compartments.

(b) Each compartment should have at least one other escape route, independent of the route into the adjoining compartment (see Diagram 6). This other route may be by way of a third compartment, provided that compartment contains a storey exit which is not by way of another compartment, and which is independent from the exits from the other compartments.

Where the above conditions have been met, for the purpose of travel distance (see 1.2.2.2), a door in a compartment wall may be regarded as being equivalent to a storey exit.

Diagram 6 **Progressive horizontal evacuation** *Par. 1.2.7.3*

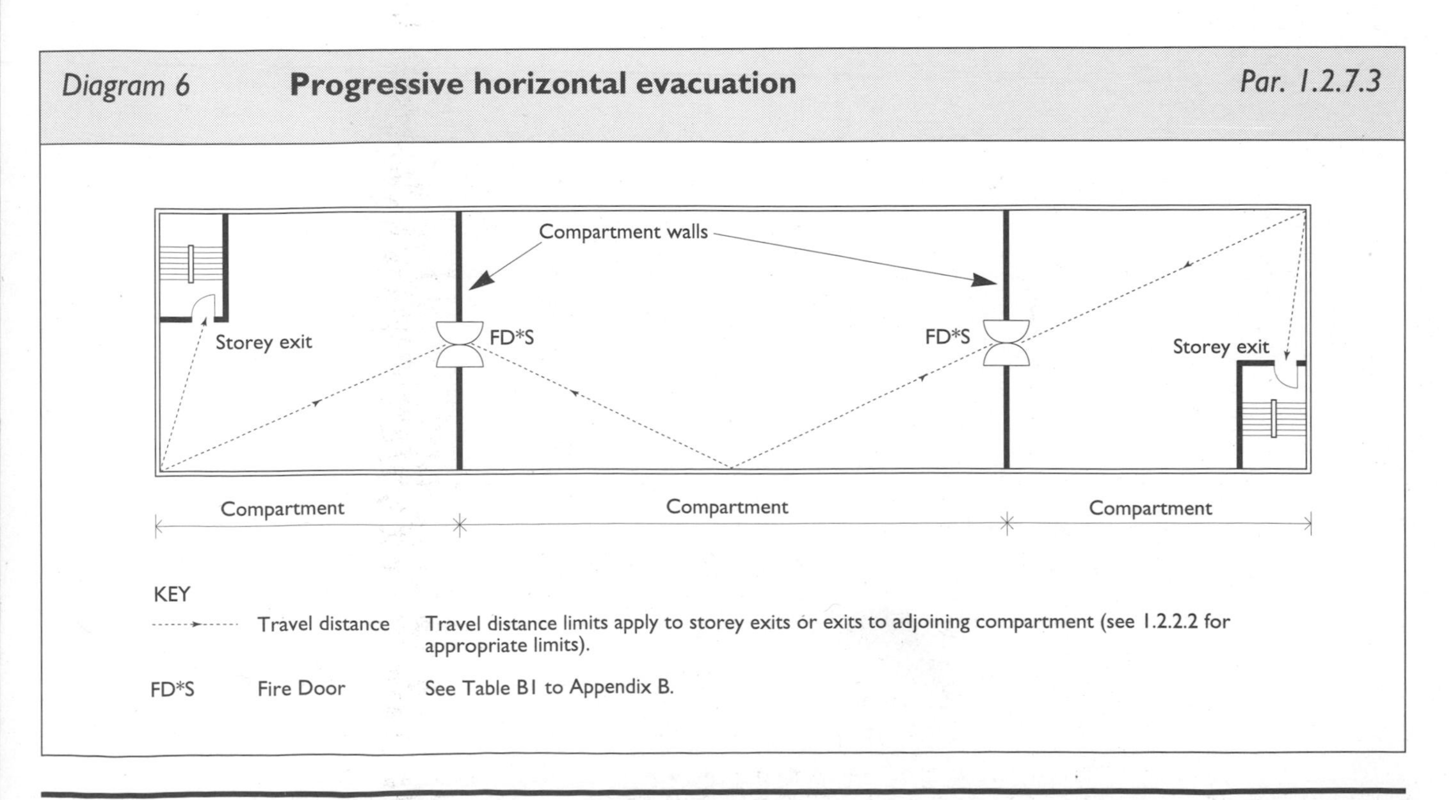

1.2.8 Closely-Seated Audiences

There are particular problems that arise when people are limited in their ability to escape by fixed seating. Any such arrangements made for a closely seated audience (or seated spectators) should meet the provisions set out in Section 3, Sub-Section 8, to BS 5588: Part 6: 1991.

1.2.9 Premises provided with a Stage

Stage areas present particular problems in that they present additional fire risk from the presence of combustible materials. Where stage areas occur they should comply with the provisions for these areas set out in Section 5, Sub-Section 13, to BS 5588: Part 6: 1991.

1.3 Design for Vertical Escape

1.3.1 Introduction

An important aspect of means of escape in multi-storey buildings is the availability of a sufficient number of adequately-sized and protected escape stairways. This Section deals with these matters, including measures necessary to protect escape stairways, for all types of building other than those covered by codes of practice or other documents which are referred to in sub-section 1.1.

It should be read in conjunction with the general provisions for means of escape in sub-section 1.4.

1.3.2 Number of Escape Stairways

1.3.2.1 The number of escape stairways needed in a building (or part of a building) will be determined by:

(a) the constraints imposed in sub-section 1.2 on the design of horizontal escape routes;

(b) whether independent stairways are required in mixed occupancy buildings (see 1.3.2.3 below);

(c) whether a single stairway is acceptable (see par. 1.3.3); and

(d) provision of adequate width for escape (see paragraph 1.3.4).

1.3.2.2 In larger buildings, provisions for access for the fire service may apply. Some escape stairways may need to serve also as fire-fighting stairways. The number of escape stairways may therefore be affected by the requirements of B5 (see 5.3).

1.3.2.3 Where a building contains storeys, or parts of storeys, in different purpose groups and if one of those purpose groups is either assembly and recreation or residential it should have means of escape which are independent of any other purpose group except for the conditions described below.

In a building with not more than four storeys above ground or access level, a stairway may serve both dwellings and non-residential occupancies where:

- the stairway is separated from each occupancy by protected lobbies (see 1.3.8) at all levels; and
- an automatic fire detection and alarm system is provided throughout the building (see 1.4.14).

In a building with more than four storeys above ground or access level, a stairway serving a flat or maisonette should not communicate with other non-residential occupancies unless:

- the flat or maisonette is ancillary to the main use of the building;
- the stairway is separated from each occupancy by protected lobbies (see 1.3.8) at all levels;
- an independent alternative escape route is provided from the flat or maisonette; and
- an automatic fire detection and alarm system is provided throughout the building (see 1.4.14).

1.3.3 Single Escape Stairways

The situations where a building (or part of a building) other than buildings of Purpose Group 2(a) Residential (Institutional), may be served by a single escape stairway are:

(a) if there is no storey with a floor level in the case of a Purpose Group 5 building more than 5 m above ground level, or in other cases more than 10 m above ground level, and where (in accordance with par. 1.2.2.5) every storey may have a single escape route, or

(b) if there is a basement the floor of which is not more than 3 m below ground level where (in accordance with par. 1.2.2.5) every basement storey may have a single escape route.

1.3.4 Width of Escape Stairways

The width of escape stairways should:

(a) be not less than the width(s) required for any exit(s) affording access to them;

(b) conform with the minimum widths given in Table 1.5;

(c) not exceed 1400 mm if serving any storeys more than 30 m above ground level; and

(d) not narrow at any point on their way to a final exit.

If the width of the stairway is more than 1800 mm, then for reasons of safety in use the stairway should have a central handrail. In such a case the stairway width on each side of the handrail needs to be considered separately for the purpose of assessing stairway capacity.

Where an exit route from a stairway also forms the escape route from the ground and/or basement storeys, the width may need to be increased accordingly.

In buildings of Purpose Group 2(a) Residential (Institutional), any landing associated with a stairway forming part of an escape route should be adequate for the purposes of evacuation. Where evacuation of beds or mattresses by way of a stairway is likely to be required, any landing associated with such a stairway should have a width not less than 2800 mm and a depth clear of obstructions not less than 1950 mm.

1.3.5 Calculation of Minimum Stairway Width

1.3.5.1 General - Every escape stairway should be wide enough to accommodate the number of persons needing to use it in an emergency. This will depend on the number of stairways provided and whether the escape strategy is based on the total or phased evacuation of the building (or part of the building).

Escape based on total evacuation should be used for:

(a) all stairs serving basements;

(b) all stairs serving buildings with open spatial planning; and

(c) all stairs serving Residential or Assembly and recreation buildings.

Paragraph 1.3.5.3 deals with the concept of total evacuation. Table 1.6 assumes the total evacuation of all storeys simultaneously.

Paragraph 1.3.5.4 deals with the concept of phased evacuation, and sets out the special measures that are necessary if a system of phased evacuation is used. Table 1.7 assumes the phased evacuation of not more than two floors at a time, and should be used for buildings over 30 m high, provided that the building is not one that is identified in the previous paragraph as needing to be designed on the basis of

Table 1.5 **Minimum width of escape stairways**

	Situation	Maximum number of persons (1)	Minimum width (mm)
1	In any building, and serving an area which can accommodate more than 100 people.	150 220 More than 220	1000 1100 5 mm per person(2)(3)
2	In a building of Purpose Group 2(a), Residential (Institutional), (unless it will be used only by staff).		1150 (4)
3	In a building of Purpose Group 5, Assembly and recreation, serving an area which can accommodate less than 100 people.	100	900
4	Any stairway not described above.	50 100	800 900

Notes:
(1) Assessed as likely to use the stairway in a fire or emergency.
(2) See 1.3.5.3 and Table 1.6 for capacity of stairways when designing for total evacuation of the building.
(3) See 1.3.5.4 and Table 1.7 minimum aggregate width of stairways designed for phased evacuation.
(4) Except in the case of an existing building.

total evacuation.

Buildings, other than those identified above as needing to be designed on the basis of total evacuation which are less than 30 m high may also be designed on the basis of phased evacuation if the provisions in par. 1.3.5.4 are met.

1.3.5.2 Discounting of stairways - Whichever method of evacuation is used, where two or more stairways are provided it should be assumed that one of them might not be available due to fire or smoke. It is therefore necessary to discount each stairway in turn in order to ensure that the capacity of the remaining stairways is adequate for the number of persons needing to escape.

An exception to the provision to discount stairways in turn is if every escape stairway is approached on each storey through a protected lobby. In such a case the likelihood of a stairway not being available is significantly reduced and it is not necessary to discount a stairway. A protected lobby need not be provided on the topmost storey for the exception to apply. Another exception is if the stairways are protected by a suitable pressurization system. A design method for pressurization of escape routes is set out in BS 5588: Part 4. The discounting of one stairway applies to a building fitted with a sprinkler system, unless the stairways are lobbied or provided with a pressurization system as described above.

The exceptions listed above to the requirement for discounting each stairway in turn should not be applied to :

(i) assembly and recreation (Purpose Group 5) buildings;

(ii) any building where, by virtue of the limits on travel distance and/or numbers of occupants, less than three stairways are required;

(iii) any building with a storey more than 20 m above ground level.

As with the design of horizontal escape routes, where the maximum number of people needing to use the escape stairway is not known, the appropriate capacity should be calculated on the basis of the occupant capacity. Guidance is set out in paragraph 1.0.10 and Table 1.1 of this Technical Guidance Document.

1.3.5.3 Total evacuation - In a building designed for total evacuation, the escape stairways should have the capacity to allow all floors to be evacuated simultaneously. Persons on the lower floors will evacuate from the building quicker than those on the upper floors and account is also taken of persons within the stairways during the evacuation process.

Table 1.6 gives capacities, based on total evacuation, for stairways of different widths (1000 mm to 1800 mm) and numbers of storeys served (1 to 10).

Table 1.6 has been derived from the formula:

$$P = 200w + 50(w - 0.3)(n - 1)$$, where:

P: is the number of people that can be accommodated;

w: is the width of the stairway in metres; and

n: is the number of storeys served.

The formula above may be used as an alternative to Table 1.6 or for more than 10 storeys.

The widths of stairways provided should also meet the criteria indicated at 1.3.4 and take account of the need, where required, to discount any one stairway (see 1.3.5.2).

Table 1.6	**Capacities of stairways (Total Evacuation)**								
Number of storeys served	**Maximum number of persons accommodated on one stair of width:(mm)**								
	1000	**1100**	**1200**	**1300**	**1400**	**1500**	**1600**	**1700**	**1800**
1	150	220	240	260	280	300	320	340	360
2	190	260	285	310	335	360	385	410	435
3	230	300	330	360	390	420	450	480	510
4	270	340	375	410	445	480	515	550	585
5	310	380	420	460	500	540	580	620	660
6	350	420	465	510	555	600	645	690	735
7	390	460	510	560	610	660	710	760	810
8	430	500	555	610	665	720	775	830	885
9	470	540	600	660	720	780	840	900	960
10	510	580	645	710	775	840	905	970	1035

Note: The capacity of stairs serving more than 10 floors may be obtained by the formula at 1.3.5.3.

1.3.5.4 Phased evacuation - The concept of phased evacuation is based on evacuating persons on a sequential basis, commencing with those on the storeys most affected by the fire in its initial stages. That is the storey of fire origin and the one immediately above. By designing on the basis of phased evacuation, stairway widths less than those needed for total evacuation are possible. However, a package of compensatory features are needed. These are set out below:

(a) the stairways should be approached through a protected lobby or protected corridor at each storey except a top storey consisting exclusively of plant rooms;

(b) every floor should be a compartment floor;

(c) if the building has a storey with a floor over 30 m above ground level, the building should be protected throughout by an automatic sprinkler system meeting the relevant recommendations of BS 5306 Fire extinguishing installations and equipment on premises: Part 2: Specification for sprinkler systems, i.e. the relevant occupancy rating together with the additional requirements for life safety.

(d) the building should be fitted with an appropriate fire detection and alarm system (see 1.4.14);

(e) an internal speech communication system, such as a telephone or intercom system, should be provided to permit conversation between a control point at fire service access level, and a fire warden on every storey.

The minimum width of stairway designed on the basis of phased evacuation is indicated in Table 1.7. This table assumes a phased evacuation of not more than two floors at a time.

The success of a system of phased evacuation depends to a large extent on the satisfactory functioning of the measures outlined above. Arrangements for the proper maintenance of the systems are necessary, as are arrangements for proper management and training. These matters are not appropriate for control under Building Regulations, but satisfactory arrangements may be sought under other legislation relevant to the occupancy.

Table 1.7	**Minimum aggregate width of stairways for phased evacuation**
Maximum number of persons in any storey	**Stairway width (mm)**
100	1000
120	1100
130	1200
140	1300
150	1400
160	1500
170	1600
180	1700
190	1800

Notes:

1 As an alternative to using Table 1.7, where the maximum number of persons in any storey exceeds 100 the minimum width of a stairway may be calculated from - ((P x 10) - 100) mm, where P = the number of people on the most heavily occupied floor.

2 See Table 1.5 for minimum width of escape stairways. See 1.3.4 (c) if the stairway serves any storey more than 30 m above ground level.

1.3.6 Protection of Escape Stairways

1.3.6.1 General - Escape stairways need to have a satisfactory standard of fire protection if they are to fulfil their role as areas of relative safety during a fire evacuation. Protection of escape stairways is provided by enclosure of the stairway by fire-resisting construction. Certain situations (see 1.3.8) require the additional protection provided by a protected access lobby or corridor to the stairway.

In certain situations such as from a gallery, an open stairway may form part of an escape route conforming with the constraints of sub-section 1.2, but such a stairway may not be regarded as an escape stairway of the type described above.

Escape stairways should conform with the provisions in pars. 1.3.6.2 to 1.3.6.6 below.

1.3.6.2 Enclosure of escape stairways - Every escape stairway, unless it is an external escape stairway (see 1.3.9), should be situated within a fire-resisting enclosure (i.e. it should be a protected stairway).

There may be additional provisions if the stairway is also a protected shaft (where it penetrates one or more compartment floors, see Section B3) or if it is a fire-fighting stairway (see Section B5).

The performance requirements for the enclosure to a protected stairway are indicated in Appendix A (Tables A1 and A2). The performance requirements for doors to the enclosure are contained in Appendix B (Table B1).

1.3.6.3 Exits from protected stairways - Every protected stairway should discharge:

(a) directly to a final exit; or

(b) by way of a protected exit passageway to a final exit.

1.3.6.4 Separation of adjoining stairways - Where two protected stairways (or exit passageways leading to different final exits) are adjacent, they should be separated by an imperforate enclosure.

1.3.6.5 Use of space within protected stairways - A protected stairway needs to be relatively free of potential sources of fire. Consequently, items that may be incorporated in a protected stairway are limited to the following:

(a) sanitary accommodation or washrooms are permitted, provided that the accommodation is not used as a cloakroom. A gas water heater or sanitary incinerator may be installed in the accommodation, but the accommodation should not include any other gas appliance.

(b) a lift may be included in a protected stairway. There are other provisions about lifts in Section 1.4.9.

(c) if the protected stairway serves part of a building that has access to at least one other escape stairway, then a reception or enquiry area may be included in the stairway at ground or access level. The reception or enquiry area should not be more than 10 m^2 in area. Cupboards enclosed with fire-resisting construction may also be included in such a protected stairway.

1.3.6.6 Fire resistance and openings in external walls of protected stairways - With some configurations of external wall, a fire in one part of a building could subject the external wall, of a protected stairway to heat (for example, where the two are adjacent at an internal angle in the facade as shown in Diagram 7). If the external wall of the protected stairway has little fire resistance, there is a risk that this could prevent the safe use of the stairway.

Where a protected stairway projects beyond, or is recessed from, or is in an internal angle of, the adjoining external wall of the building, then the distance between any unprotected area in the external enclosures to the building and any unprotected area in the enclosure to the stairway should be at least 1.8 m (see Diagram 7).

1.3.6.7 Gas service pipes in protected stairways - Pipes intended to carry gaseous or liquid fuels or associated matters should not be incorporated within a protected stairway.

1.3.6.8 Separation of high fire risk areas - Escape stairways require a high degree of protection from fire. Rooms or other accommodation which have doors opening onto escape stairways can threaten the escape routes from a building. Places of special fire risk (see 1.0.9) should therefore be located so that they do not communicate directly with the enclosure to a protected stairway.

1.3.7 Basement Stairways

Because of their situation, basement stairways are more likely to be filled with smoke and heat than are stairways in ground and upper storeys. Special measures are therefore needed in order to prevent a basement fire causing a hazard to upper storeys. These are set out in the paragraphs below.

1.3.7.1 If an escape stairway forms part of the only escape route from an upper storey of a building (or part of a building) it should not be continued down to serve any basement storey. Any escape stairway between a basement and the ground storey should be separated by a protected lobby or protected corridor from the stairway serving the upper storeys.

1.3.7.2 If there is more than one escape stairway from an upper storey of a building (or part of a building), only one of the stairways serving the upper storeys of the building (or part) need be terminated at ground level. Other stairways may connect with the basement storey(s) if they are separated at each basement level by a protected lobby or protected corridor.

1.3.8 Protected Lobbies and Corridors to Escape Stairways

1.3.8.1 Provision of protected lobbies and corridors - In addition to stairways serving basements (see 1.3.7), there are other situations where an escape stairway requires the added protection of a protected lobby or corridor. These are:

(a) where the stairway is the only stairway serving a building (or part of a building) which has three or more storeys (see Appendix C, Diagram 36), except in the case in a small guesthouse (see 1.3.8.2);

Diagram 7 **External protection to protected stairway** *Par. 1.3.6.6*

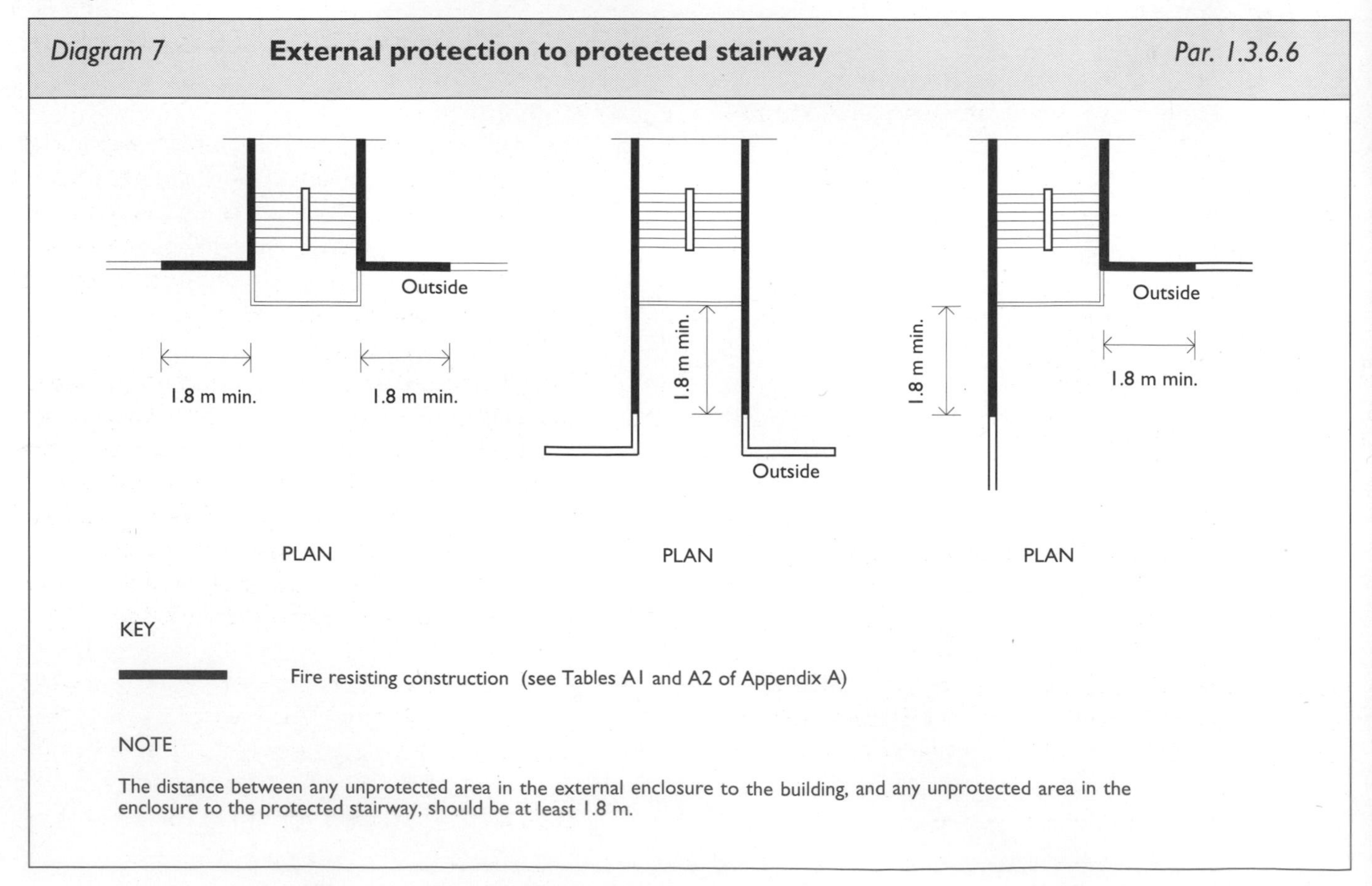

NOTE

The distance between any unprotected area in the external enclosure to the building, and any unprotected area in the enclosure to the protected stairway, should be at least 1.8 m.

(b) where the stairway serves any storey at a height greater than 20 m (see Appendix C, Diagram 38);

(c) where the building is designed for phased evacuation (see 1.3.5.4);

(d) between a protected stairway and a place of special fire risk (see 1.0.9);

(e) in a sprinklered building in which the stairway width has not been based on discounting one stairway (see 1.3.5.2); or

(f) in a building serving flats and maisonettes and other non-residential occupancy (see 1.3.2.3).

in the above mentioned situations, access to the protected stairway should be by way of protected lobbies or protected corridors at all storey levels, except at the top-most level.

1.3.8.2 Small guesthouses (Purpose Group 2(b)) - An exception to the requirement for a protected lobby or corridor to the stairway in a building served by a single escape stairway may be made in the case of a guesthouse (Purpose Group 2(b)), where the following conditions are met:

(i) the house does not contain a basement and there are not more than three storeys (see Diagram 36);

(ii) there are not more than four bedrooms on any upper storey;

(iii) the stairway is a protected stairway (see 1.3.6.2);

(iv) a fire detection and alarm system is provided in accordance with the requirements of par. 1.4.14; and

(v) all habitable rooms are provided with windows which can be used for escape or rescue (see 1.5.6).

1.3.8.3 Existing buildings - In the case of some existing buildings, the provision of protected lobbies or corridors to an existing escape stairway may not be practicable. In these situations, it would be appropriate to consider alternative solutions and the provision of compensating features (see 1.0.11.2 and 1.0.11.3). The nature and extent of the additional measures required will depend on the circumstances of each particular case.

Where protected lobbies or corridors can not be provided, it will be necessary to consider the following items in the context of the need to ensure a satisfactory level of protection to the means of escape:

- the nature and extent of the occupancies and accommodation adjoining the protected stairway;
- the fire performance of the stairway enclosure;
- the performance of fire door assemblies as installed in the building (see Appendix B);
- smoke control measures to protect the stairway enclosure; and
- life safety protection to be provided by the fire detection and alarm system (see 1.4.14).

1.3.8.4 Requirements for protected lobbies and corridors - Every protected lobby or corridor which is required to be provided should comply with the following:-

(i) be constructed with walls having fire resistance as required in Section B3 for the protecting structure of the stairway, and any door to the lobby should be a self-closing fire door having a fire resistance not less than half that required for the wall, but not less than 30 minutes;

(ii) be constructed so that the clearance between the edges of the doors when fully open is not less than 500 mm, and the distance between the doors in the closed position is not less than 1 m, or when the distance between any two doors in the closed position is less than 1 m, the planes of such doors are at an angle to one another of not less than 90 degrees; and

(iii) be ventilated by means of permanent openings to the open air having an area of not less than 0.05 m^2, or 0.4 m^2 where the protected lobby or corridor connects the stairway with an enclosed car park, a basement, or an area of special fire risk. Where the lobby or corridor is not adjacent to an external wall of the building any connecting ventilation duct-work should be protected by fire-resisting construction.

1.3.9 External Escape Stairways

In limited situations (see 1.2.6) external stairways are acceptable as forming part of an escape route. It is important that the external stairway is sufficiently protected from the weather and is adequately protected from a fire in the building. The following conditions should be met:

(a) unless the stairway is of limited height, it should be protected from the effects of snow and ice. The degree of protection required will depend on the location of the stairway and the protection that might be afforded to the stairway by the building itself. Weather protection is not required if the stairway serves a floor or storey which is not more than 6 m above the external ground level.

(b) all doors affording access to the stairway should be fire-resisting, except that a fire-resisting door is not required at the head of any stairway leading downwards and where there is only one exit from the building onto the top landing;

(c) any part of the external walls identified below should be of fire-resisting construction -

   (i) within 1.8 m of, and 9 m vertically below, the flights and landings of a stairway leading downwards; and

   (ii) within 1.8 m of, and vertically above, the flights and landings of a stairway leading upwards; and

   (iii) within 3 m of the escape route from the foot of the stairway at ground level to a place of safety.

Note: Unprotected openings are not permitted in those parts identified above. Any doors should be fire-resisting and windows should be fire-resisting and fixed shut.

The construction of external escape stairways should comply with the requirements outlined in 1.4.4.

Diagram 8 shows two examples of unprotected external escape stairways.

Diagram 8 **External escape stairways** *Par. 1.3.9*

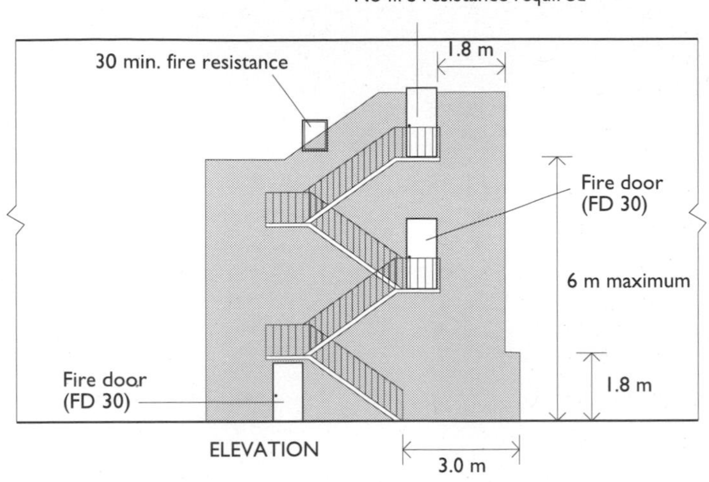

EXAMPLE A

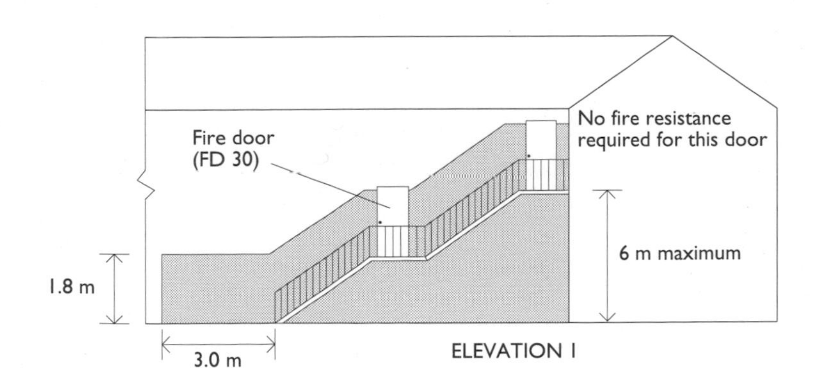

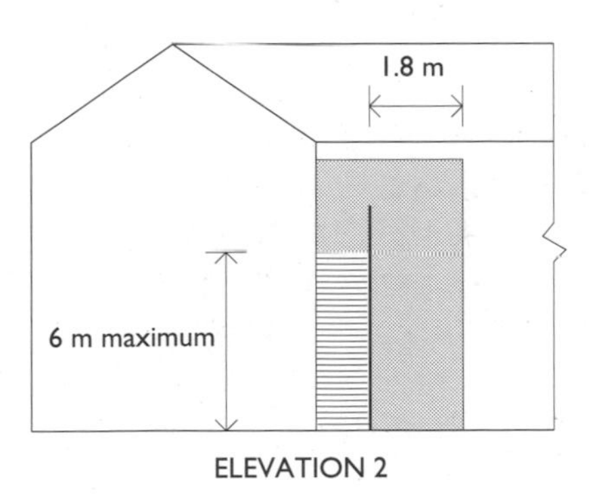

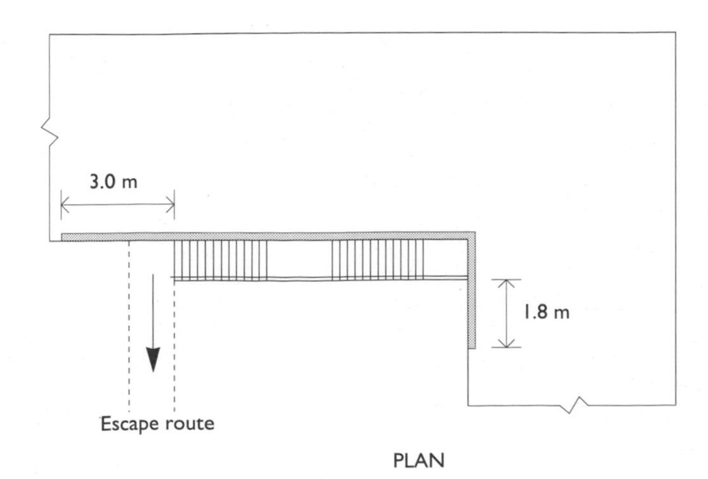

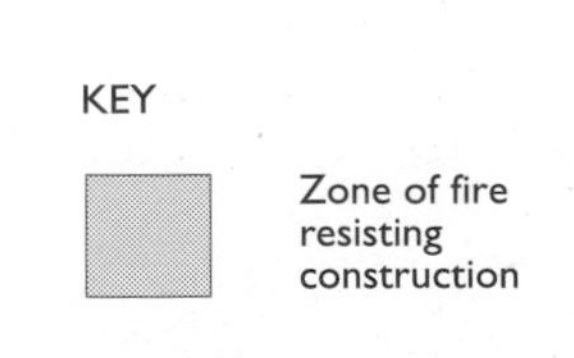

EXAMPLE B

1.4 General Provisions for Means of Escape

Introduction

1.4.1 This sub-section deals with a number of provisions about the construction and protection of escape routes generally, and about some services installations and other matters associated with the design of escape routes. It applies to all buildings other than Purpose Groups 1(a) and 1(b) - dwelling houses.

It should therefore be read in conjunction with sub-sections 1.1, 1.2 and 1.3 of this Document.

1.4.2 Protection of Escape Routes

1.4.2.1 Fire resistance of enclosures - Details of fire resistance test criteria, and standards of performance, are set out in Appendix A to this Document.

All walls, partitions and other enclosures that need to be fire-resisting to meet the provisions in this Document should have the appropriate performance given in Tables A1 and A2 of Appendix A. They should also meet any limitations on the use of glass (see par. 1.4.2.3).

1.4.2.2 Fire resistance of doors - Details of fire resistance test criteria, and standards of performance for fire doors, are set out in Appendix B to this Document.

Note: Any reference to a fire door in this Technical Guidance Document, or in any code of practice or other document referred to in this Technical Guidance Document, is intended to mean a complete door assembly which includes the door leaf or leaves, the door frame, ironmongery (hinges, latches, closers, etc.) and any seals where required between the frame and leaf or between leaves, and which is installed in a building and is capable of meeting the required performance. The performance of a fire door will critically depend on the correct installation of the complete door assembly.

All doors that need to be fire-resisting to meet the provisions in this Document should have the appropriate performance given in Table B1 of Appendix B. They should also meet any limitations on the use of glass (see par. 1.4.2.3).

1.4.2.3 Fire resistance of glazed elements - Where glazed elements in fire-resisting enclosures and doors are only able to satisfy the relevant performance in terms of integrity, the use of glass is limited. These limitations are set out in Appendix A, Table A4.

Where the relevant performance can be met in terms of both integrity and insulation, there is no restriction in this Section on the use or amount of glass, but there may be some restriction under Section B5.

1.4.2.4 Protection of escape stairways - The protection of escape stairways should be in accordance with the provisions outlined at 1.3.6.

1.4.3 Doors on Escape Routes

1.4.3.1 The time taken to negotiate a closed door can be critical in an escape situation. Doors on escape routes (both within and from the building) should therefore be readily openable if undue delay is to be avoided. Accordingly the provisions in the paragraphs below should be met.

1.4.3.2 Door fastenings - In general, doors on escape routes, whether or not the doors are fire doors, should either not be fitted with lock, latch or bolt fastenings, or they should only be fitted with simple fastenings that can be readily operated in the direction of escape without the use of a key.

Where security on final exit doors is an important consideration, such as some assembly or commercial uses, panic bolts should be used to secure doors. Where additional security is required when the premises is not in use, hardware which is fully removable should be used. The following recommendations apply to buildings, or parts of buildings which are used for assembly or recreation (Purpose Group 5):-

(a) Exit doors from areas holding more than 50 people should either be free from fastenings or be fitted with panic bolts complying with BS

5725: Part 1.

(b) Doors, other than those covered by item (a), should be fitted only with simple fastenings that can be operated from the escape side of the door without the use of a key.

Attention is drawn to the provisions of the Fire Safety in Places of Assembly (Ease of Escape), Regulations, 1985 (S.I. No. 249 of 1985).

Information about door closing and hold open devices for fire doors is given in Appendix B.

1.4.3.3 Direction of opening - Doors on escape routes should be hung so that they open in the direction of escape. In the case of small rooms or buildings, this may not be practical or indeed necessary, but in the following situations doors on escape routes must always be hung to open in the direction of escape:

(a) from a place of special fire risk, or

(b) in the case of premises comprising an industrial, storage or assembly and recreation use if more than 20 people are expected to use them, or

(c) in the case of any other premises if more than 50 people are expected to use them.

An exception to the requirement for outward opening doors on escape routes may be made in the case of class-rooms and other small rooms in schools where the number of persons in such rooms does not exceed 60.

Manual sliding doors may be permitted, in certain limited circumstances only, such as doors from rooms in industrial or storage buildings which are occupied by not more than 10 persons and where swing doors would be impracticable.

As an alternative to outward opening doors, in certain limited situations, it may be appropriate to consider the provision of doors which are held in the open position. It should not be possible for such doors to be released and closed when the building is in use.

1.4.3.4 Amount of opening and effect on associated escape routes - All doors on escape routes should be hung to open not less than 90°, and with a swing that is clear of any change of floor level, other than a threshold on the line of the doorway, and does not reduce the required width of any escape route across a landing.

Similarly, where it is necessary to recess a door that is opening towards a corridor, then the depth of recess should be sufficient that the door swing does not reduce the required width of the corridor.

1.4.3.5 Vision panels - These are needed where doors on escape routes subdivide corridors, or where the doors are hung to swing both ways.

1.4.3.6 Revolving and automatic doors - Revolving doors, automatic doors and turnstiles can obstruct the passage of persons escaping. These types of doors should not be provided across escape routes unless:

(i) they are automatic doors complying with BS 7036: and either:

 (a) they are arranged to fail safely to outward opening from any position of opening; or

 (b) they are provided with a monitored fail safe system for opening the doors if the mains power supply fails; or

(ii) swing doors to the required width are provided immediately adjacent.

1.4.4 Construction of Escape Stairways

1.4.4.1 General - Every escape stairway and its associated landings should be constructed of materials of limited combustibility in the following situations.

(a) if it is the only stairway serving the building, or part of the building, and the period of fire resistance for the elements of structure (Tables A1, A2 to Appendix A) is 60 minutes or more,

(b) if it is within a basement storey,

(c) if it serves any storey having a floor level more than 20 m above ground or access level, or

(d) if it is an external stairway
(there are other provisions about external escape stairways in par. 1.3.9).

In satisfying the above provision, combustible materials may be added to the upper surface of these stairways, except in the case of firefighting stairs.

An exception to the requirement for escape stairways to be constructed of materials of limited combustibility may be made in the case of an existing internal stairway in any existing building where:

- the width of the stairway and dimensions of steps are adequate for the purposes of means of escape, and

- the stairway is of sound construction and is capable of affording safe passage for the users of the building.

There are other provisions dealing with the construction of fire fighting stairways in Section B5.

Escape stairways should comply with the requirements of Section 1 of Technical Guidance Document K - Stairways, Ramps and Guards, to the Building Regulations, 1997. An exception to this requirement may be made in the case of an existing stairway in an existing building which is capable of affording safe passage for the users of the building.

1.4.4.2 Helical, spiral stairways and fixed ladders - Helical and spiral stairways and fixed ladders may form part of an escape route subject to the following restrictions:

(a) Helical and Spiral stairways should comply with the recommendations of BS 5395 Stairs, ladder and walkways: Part 2 Code of Practice for the design of helical and spiral stairs. If they are intended to serve members of the public, they should meet the requirements for a type E (public) stairway to that standard.

(b) In the case of fixed ladders, these should only be intended for use by able-bodied adults, and in circumstances where it is not practical to provide a more satisfactory means of vertical egress. Fixed ladders are acceptable within plant rooms.

In addition, fixed ladders should be constructed of non-combustible materials.

Guidance on the design of Helical and Spiral stairways and fixed ladders, from the aspect of safety in use, is given in Technical Guidance Document K.

1.4.5 Height of Escape Routes

All escape routes should have a minimum clear headroom of not less than 2 m and there should be no projection below this height, except for any door frame, which would impede the free flow of persons using them.

1.4.6 Floors of Escape Routes

The floors of all escape routes (including steps, ramps and landings) should have non-slippery even surfaces.

Where a ramp forms part of an escape route, it should not be steeper than 1 in 12 if it is shorter than 9 m, otherwise it should not be steeper than 1 in 20.

Any sloping floor or tier should be constructed with a pitch of not more than 35° to the horizontal.

Further guidance on the design of ramps and associated landings, from the aspect of safety in use, is given in Technical Guidance Documents K and M.

1.4.7 Final Exits

Final exits need to be dimensioned and sited so that they facilitate the evacuation of persons out of the building, and away from the building. Accordingly, they should be not less in width than the escape route(s) they serve and also meet the following provisions in the paragraphs below.

Final exits should be sited to ensure rapid dispersal of persons from the vicinity of the building so that they are no longer in danger from fire and smoke. Direct access to a street, passageway, walkway or open space should be available. The route clear of the building should be well defined, and suitably guarded if necessary, in situations where the exit discharges other than to an open street or open space at street level.

Final exits also need to be apparent to persons who may need to use them. This is particularly important where the exit opens off a stairway that continues down, or up, beyond the level of the final exit.

Final exits also need to be sited so that they are clear of any risk from fire or smoke in a basement, or from openings to transformer chambers, boiler rooms and similar risks.

1.4.8 Lighting of Escape Routes

1.4.8.1 The safe movement of persons along escape routes, towards and through the exits to a place safety, depends on the illumination of those routes and the ability to see hazards and changes of level and direction. Adequate artificial lighting should be provided to all internal and external escape routes, except in the case where there is adequate natural lighting and the building is used only during daylight hours.

1.4.8.2 In the event of failure of the normal lighting, emergency escape lighting is required. Emergency escape lighting is required to ensure that lighting is provided promptly, automatically and for a suitable duration when the normal lighting fails. Emergency escape lighting is required on complete failure of the power supplies to the normal lighting in the building and also on a localised failure of the normal lighting.

1.4.8.3 Emergency escape lighting should be provided:

(a) to indicate clearly and unambiguously the escape routes so that the means of escape can be safely and effectively used;

(b) to provide illumination along such routes to allow safe movement towards and through the exits provided;

(c) to ensure that fire alarm call points and first-aid fire fighting equipment, where provided, can be readily located.

Note: Emergency escape lighting may also be required for the purpose of the Safety, Health and Welfare at Work Act, 1989 to enable work activities to be safely terminated and allow other emergency actions to be effectively carried out. Additional emergency escape lighting may also be required under the Fire Services Act, 1981 when the building is in use. The provisions outlined in this Section may need to be supplemented accordingly.

1.4.8.4 Emergency escape lighting should be provided in accordance with the provisions indicated in Table 1.8. For the purpose of this table the emergency escape lighting may consist of the following parts:

(i) un-defined escape routes: open areas in a building where the escape routes are not fixed or defined by the elements of construction;

(ii) defined escape routes: routes, such as exits, escape corridors and escape stairways, through which or along which, persons may be required to travel to reach a final exit from a building;

(iii) external escape routes: those parts of an escape route outside a building from a final exit, which may be required for persons to reach a place of safety.

1.4.8.5 Emergency escape lighting should be designed and installed in accordance with the relevant recommendations in I.S. 3217: 1989 Code of practice for emergency lighting.

1.4.9 Lifts

1.4.9.1 Evacuation lifts - In general it is not appropriate to use lifts when there is a fire in the building because there is always the danger of the lift becoming immobilised as a result of the fire, and of persons being trapped inside. However, in some circumstances a lift may be needed as part of a management plan for evacuating disabled persons. In such cases the lift installation needs to be appropriately sited and protected, and needs to contain a number of safety features that are intended to ensure that the lift may remain usable for evacuation purposes during the fire.

Table 1.8	**Provision of emergency escape lighting**	
Use of building or part of building	**Purpose Group[1]**	**Parts requiring emergency escape lighting**
Flats	1(c)	Defined escape routes, other than within dwellings.
Residential (Institutional)	2(a)	Defined escape routes, wards, treatment rooms, communal rooms, bathrooms and toilet areas, kitchens, other habitable rooms over 30 m^2 in area.
Other residential	2(b)	Defined escape routes, dormitories, common rooms, kitchens, other habitable rooms over 30 m^2 in area.
Offices	3	Defined escape routes.
Shops	4(a)	Defined and un-defined escape routes.[2]
Shopping Centre	4(b)	Defined and un-defined escape routes within individual shop units and in mall and concourse areas.
Assembly and recreation	5	Defined and un-defined escape routes.[3]
Industrial	6	Defined escape routes.
Storage	7	Defined escape routes.
Other non-residential	8	Defined escape routes, common areas, habitable rooms over 30 m^2 in area.
Any use other than dwelling houses	1(c), 2 to 8	Emergency generator room, switch room, plant room, battery room for emergency lighting system.
Any use other than dwelling houses	1(c), 2 to 8	External escape routes as required.[4]

Notes:

(1) as defined in Table 0.1

(2) except a shop at ground floor with a sales area less than 100 m^2 and maximum travel distance of 15 m to a final exit to a public area.

(3) except in accommodation open on one side, with naturally lit escape routes, to view sport or entertainment during normal daylight hours; and except toilet accommodation having a floor area of not more than 8 m^2.

(4) except where there is sufficient external lighting from a public or other independent power supply.

Guidance on the necessary measures is given in BS 5588: Part 8 : 1988.

1.4.9.2 Fire protection of lift installations generally - Because lifts by their nature connect floors, there is the possibility that they may prejudice escape routes. To safeguard against this, the following provisions in the paragraphs below should be met.

Lifts, which rise within a large volume such as a mall or atrium, and do not have a conventional lift-well, may be at risk if they run through a smoke reservoir. In these cases care is needed to maintain the integrity of any smoke reservoir, and protect the occupants of the lift.

Lift wells should be either contained within the enclosures of a protected stairway, or be enclosed throughout their height with fire-resisting construction if they are sited such as to prejudice the means of escape. A lift well connecting different compartments should form a protected shaft (see Section B3, 3.2).

Lifts should be approached only by way of a protected lobby (or protected corridor) in basements, or in any storey that contains high fire risk areas and where the lift also delivers directly into corridors serving sleeping accommodation. Examples of high fire risk areas in this context are kitchens, lounges and stores. In buildings with any storey at a height greater than 20 m, lifts should be approached by way of a protected lobby (see 1.3.8).

A lift should not be continued down to serve any basement storey if it is in a building (or part of a building) served by only one escape stairway, or within the enclosures to an escape stairway which is terminated at ground level.

Sub-section 1.3 sets out restrictions on escape stairways that connect basements with the upper storeys of a building.

Lift machine rooms should be sited over the lift well whenever possible. If the lift well is within the enclosures to a protected stairway being the only stairway serving the building (or part of the building), then the machine room should be located outside the stairway if it cannot be sited above the lift well.

1.4.10 Electrical Installations and Protected Circuits

The electrical installation, comprising wiring, sockets, switches, fuse boards, distribution boards, circuit breakers, etc., should be installed in accordance with the National Rules for Electrical Installations (ET 101) published by the Electro-Technical Council of Ireland.

There are situations, such as in the case of fire alarm systems, emergency lighting or evacuation lifts, where continued operation of certain electrical components during a fire may be required. In this regard, the specific provisions of the appropriate design standards indicated in this Technical Guidance Document should be followed.

1.4.11 Ventilation Systems

1.4.11.1 Natural ventilation - Guidance on designing for natural ventilation is contained in BS 5925 : 1991, Code of Practice for ventilation principles and designing for natural ventilation.

1.4.11.2 Mechanical ventilation and air conditioning systems - Any system of mechanical ventilation should be designed to ensure that in a fire the air movement is directed away from protected escape routes and exits. In the case of a system which recirculates air, the system should meet the relevant recommendation for recirculating distribution systems in BS: 5588: Part 9 Code of practice for ventilation and air-conditioning ductwork in terms of its operation under fire conditions.

Any system of mechanical ventilation in an assembly and recreation building should also comply with the relevant provisions below:

(a) any such system serving the parts of the premises to which the public are admitted should be independent of the remainder of the premises;

(b) if the premises is used for stage presentations, any such system should be designed to ensure that the air movement during performances is directed from the auditorium towards the stage;

(c) any such system above a stage provided with a proscenium opening should be entirely independent of the auditorium system.

Where a pressurization system is installed, any ventilation and air conditioning systems should be compatible with it.

Guidance and additional recommendations in relation to ventilation systems in Places of Assembly are contained in Section 20 of BS 5588: Part 6: 1991.

Guidance on the design and installation of mechanical ventilation and air conditioning plant is given in BS 5720: 1979 Code of practice for mechanical ventilation and air conditioning in buildings, and on ventilation and air conditioning ductwork in BS 5588: Part 9: 1989 Code of practice for ventilation and air conditioning ductwork.

1.4.12 Refuse Chutes and Storage

(a) Refuse storage chambers, refuse chutes and refuse hoppers should be sited and constructed in accordance with BS 5906:1980. Code of practice for storage and on-site treatment of solid waste from buildings.

(b) Refuse chutes and rooms provided for the storage of refuse should:

    (i) be separated from other parts of the building with fire-resisting construction (refer to Section B3), and

(ii) not be located within protected stairways or protected lobbies;

(c) Rooms containing refuse chutes, or provided for the storage of refuse, should be approached only by way of a protected lobby provided with not less than 0.2 m^2 of permanent ventilation, to the outside of the building.

(d) Access to refuse storage chambers should not be sited adjacent to escape routes or final exits or near to windows of dwellings.

1.4.13 Fire Safety Signs

Signs to indicate escape routes, including any doorways or exits which provide access to the means of escape, are required in all buildings, except within dwellings. They should be illuminated by means of natural lighting, artificial lighting or by emergency escape lighting, as appropriate (see 1.4.8), so that they are clearly visible and distinguishable by the occupants of a building.

Signs should be provided to indicate the position of fire-fighting equipment (see 1.4.16) and fire alarm call points (see 1.4.14), where provided.

Signs, in accordance with BS 5499: Part 1: 1990, should be provided on fire doors (see Appendix B), except those held open by electromagnetic devices connected to the fire alarm, to indicate that they should be kept shut.

Attention is drawn to possible additional requirements for fire safety signs under the Fire Services Act, 1981, when the building is in use.

Attention is also drawn to Statutory Instrument, S.I. No. 132 of 1995 Safety, Health and Welfare at Work (Signs) Regulations, 1995. These Regulations require the provision of emergency and other signs in a place of work, as defined in the Safety, Health and Welfare at Work Act, 1989. The shape, colours and pictogram (to convey the appropriate safety message) for the signs are prescribed in those Regulations. The relevant emergency escape and fire-fighting equipment signs may be used for the purposes of this Section (B1). Other signs, which may be required when the building is in use, are outside the scope of the Building Regulations.

1.4.14 Fire Detection and Alarm Systems

1.4.14.1 Introduction - The occurrence of fire in a building could lead to a situation where conditions become untenable and escape routes become unusable. It is likely that these conditions will not occur until some time after the initiation of the fire and the sooner the outbreak is detected, the more time will be available for evacuation, should this be necessary.

Buildings should be provided with a fire detection and alarm system to warn the occupants of the existence of fire where the building is of such a size, layout or occupancy that the fire itself may not provide adequate warning to the occupants so as to enable them to escape safely.

Where a fire detection and alarm system is provided, the system should comply with the recommendations relevant to design and installation contained in I.S. 3218: 1989 Code of practice for fire detection and alarm systems for buildings - system design, installation and servicing. The type of system to be provided should be appropriate to the uses(s) of the building and for the protection of life (types L and M systems). Guidance on the fire detection and alarm systems for certain building types is contained in the following paragraphs.

1.4.14.2 Residential (Institutional) buildings - In most types of residential (institutional) buildings, a high level of protection is required and a type L1 fire detection and alarm system should generally be provided. In the design of such systems, consideration should also be given to the category of occupant, evacuation procedures and means of alerting the emergency services.

Guidance on the provision of fire detection and alarm systems in hospitals is contained in Firecode Health Technical Memorandum 82 Alarm and detection systems, 1996.

1.4.14.3 Mixed-user buildings - A fire detection and alarm system should be provided in buildings which contain a number of different occupancy types or uses. The type of system and the degree of protection provided should be appropriate to the nature of the occupancies and to the building size, layout and construction.

1.4.14.4 Buildings containing flats or maisonettes - In a building containing flats or maisonettes, purpose group 1(c), individual dwellings should be provided with a fire detection and alarm system complying with the provisions set out in 1.5.5 of this Document (a maisonette should be treated as a two storey dwelling house for this purpose).

In addition to alarms within individual dwellings, there are situations where a common fire detection and alarm system should also be provided. This will be the case in mixed occupancy type buildings (see 1.4.14.3) but may also be required in a building containing flats only.

In a building containing flats, where the compartment floors and walls (see 3.2.5) are not constructed of non-combustible materials, a type L3X fire detection and alarm system in accordance with I.S. 3218: 1989 should be provided for the protection of the common escape routes from the flat entrance doors to a place of safety.

In a building containing flats, where the compartment floors and walls (see 3.2.5) are constructed of non-combustible materials, a manual fire alarm (type M) system in accordance with I.S. 3218: 1989 should be provided in the common escape routes from the flat entrance doors to a place of safety.

The system design should incorporate measures to reduce the risk of false alarms or misuse and provide for a means of control so that a pre-determined response leading to the evacuation of the building can be initiated. Consideration could also be given, particularly in large buildings, to a system which initially warns the occupants in the areas of the building most likely to be affected by the fire.

1.4.15 Provisions for Disabled Persons

Where access for disabled people is provided to a building or part of a building in accordance with Part M of the Second Schedule to the Building Regulations, provision should also be made, in the building or part of the building (as the case may be) for appropriate means of escape for such people.

The principles underlying the design of the means of escape from a building are based on the assumption that in the event of an outbreak of fire it may be necessary to evacuate all or part of a building. Normally the evacuation will be to a place of safety outside the building, but in some cases it may be necessary to initially evacuate to a place of relative safety within the building. The management of evacuation forms an important part of the fire safety strategy for a building. While there are no provisions in the Building Regulations in relation to fire safety management (see 0.1.7), the guidance in this Document assumes that an adequate level of fire safety management will be provided when the building is in use.

In any building there may be people with disabilities which impair their mobility or limit other faculties such as sight and hearing. The evacuation of such people require special consideration. In addition, it may be necessary to consider any special requirements in the provision of fire detection and alarm systems (see 1.4.14).

Guidance on the provision of means of escape for disabled people is contained in BS 5588: Part 8: 1988 Fire precautions in the design and construction of buildings, Part 8, Code of practice for means of escape for disabled people. The principles outlined in BS 5588: Part 8 are based on the provision of refuge areas and the management of evacuation. Refuge areas are areas within a building, separated by fire-resisting construction and provided with a safe route to a storey exit, where disabled people can await assistance for their evacuation.

Refuge areas may be within the enclosure of an escape stairway, within a protected lobby or corridor leading to an escape stairway or in a compartmented part of a storey (see 3.2) which contains an escape stairway. A lift may be used for evacuation where it meets the criteria outlined in section 10 of BS 5588: Part 8.

Part M of the Second Schedule to the Building Regulations provides for access to buildings for disabled people. Technical Guidance Document M provides guidance on compliance with the requirements of Part M.

1.4.16 First-Aid Fire-Fighting Equipment

First-aid fire fighting equipment is provided in buildings to be used by the occupants, with appropriate training and where it is safe to do so, in the early stages in the development of a fire. This equipment may be a fixed installation, such as a hose reel or may be portable fire extinguishers. Portable fire extinguishers are excluded from the provisions of the building regulations but may be required when the building is in use for the purpose of the Fire Services Act, 1981 and the Safety, Health and Welfare at Work Act, 1989.

A hose reel consists of a length of tubing fitted with a shut-off nozzle and attached to a reel, with a permanent connection to a pressurized water supply. Hose-reels conforming to I.S. EN 671: Part 1: 1995 should be provided in a building, where the floor area exceeds 500 m^2, which is used as a shop (purpose group 4(a)), a shopping centre (purpose group 4(b)), industrial (purpose group 6) or for storage (purpose group 7(a), 7(b)). The installation of hose reels should comply with the relevant recommendations in BS 5306: Part 1: 1976 Fire extinguishing installations and equipment on premises, Part 1 Hydrant systems, hose reels and foam inlets.

1.4.17 Heat Producing Appliances

Heating boilers, cookers, fires for heating and other appliances which burn liquid, gaseous or solid fuel can provide a source of ignition for fires in buildings. In this regard, critical items include:

- the location of appliances in relation to escape routes;

- the provision of suitable and adequate flues, chimneys and hearths as appropriate;

- the provision of suitable and adequate ventilation;

- the provision and storage of fuel supplies.

Part J of the Second Schedule to the Building Regulations contains requirements in relation to heat producing appliances. Technical Guidance Document J - Heat producing appliances, provides guidance on how to comply with Part J of the Regulations.

Some of the documents referred to in sub-section 1.1, contain guidance in relation to heat producing appliances and building services generally. The measures may also relate to provisions appropriate to Section B3, Internal Fire Spread (Structure).

1.5 Dwelling Houses

Introduction

1.5.1 This section deals with the means of escape provisions in Residential (Dwellings), dwelling houses (Purpose Groups 1(a) and 1(b) in Table 0.1).

Note: the means of escape provisions for Residential (Dwellings) flats and maisonettes (Purpose Group 1(c) in Table 0.1) are indicated in 1.1.2.

Dwelling houses will generally have a single escape stairway and there is a risk that this may become unusable due to smoke. Protection/enclosure to the stairway is required, to an extent which varies with the number of storeys above the ground level. Windows, if suitably located and constructed, can in some situations provide an alternative means of escape. With increasing height, windows become unsuitable for escape but may be useful for rescue purposes. Early warning of fire can be achieved by the provision of an appropriate smoke detection and alarm system.

The means of escape provisions for dwelling houses are outlined in 1.5.2 and 1.5.8. 1.5.7 deals with loft conversions in existing dwelling houses and 1.5.8 contains general provisions for dwelling houses.

Dwelling Houses with no Floors more than 4.5 m above ground level (Purpose Group 1(a))

1.5.2 The following provisions apply to dwelling houses where the height of the top storey is not more than 4.5 m (see Appendix C, Diagram 38). This type of dwelling house will typically have one or two storeys:

(i) a habitable room should not be an inner room unless it is provided with a window for escape or rescue, in accordance with 1.5.6;

(ii) a stairway serving an upper storey should be enclosed by means of storey-height construction, which need not be fire-resisting, and discharge directly to the open air;

(iii) a fire detection and alarm system should be provided, in accordance with 1.5.5; and

(iv) the general provisions for dwelling houses, outlined in 1.5.8 should be met.

An open-plan type arrangement, where the stairway rises directly from the ground floor accommodation is less preferable than that described at (ii) above and is only acceptable where the following conditions are met:

- the stairway discharges to within 4.5 m of a door at the ground storey leading directly to the open air;

- the stairway does not discharge into kitchen accommodation;

- the automatic fire detection and alarm system complies with the requirements for an LD2 system in accordance with 1.5.5;

- all habitable rooms at the upper storey are provided with windows for escape or rescue in accordance with 1.5.6; and

- meets the general provisions for dwelling houses, outlined in 1.5.8.

Dwelling Houses with one Floor more than 4.5 m above ground level (Purpose Group 1(b))

1.5.3 The following provisions apply to dwelling houses where there is one storey which is at a height of more than 4.5 m (see Appendix C, Diagram 38). This type of dwelling house will typically have three storeys above ground level:

(i) a habitable room should not be an inner room unless

  - it has a floor level not more than 4.5 m above ground or access level; and

  - it is provided with a door or window for escape or rescue which complies with the provisions of par. 1.5.6;

(ii) unless the top storey is separated from the lower storey by fire-resisting construction (refer to B3 and Appendix A) and is provided with an alternative escape route leading to its own final exit, the internal stairway should:

- be a protected stairway (see 1.4.2 and Tables A1, A2);
- connect the ground and all upper storeys; and
- either deliver directly to a final exit (Diagram 9(a)) or give access to not less than two independent escape routes delivering to alternative final exits (see Diagram 9(b));

(iii) automatic smoke detection and alarms should be provided in accordance with 1.5.5; and

(iv) the general provisions for dwelling houses, outlined in par. 1.5.8 should be met.

Dwelling Houses with more than one Floor more than 4.5 m above ground level (Purpose Group 1(b))

1.5.4 The following provisions apply to dwelling houses where there are more than one storey at a height of more than 4.5 m (see Appendix C, Diagram 38). This type of dwelling house will typically have four or more storeys above ground level:

(i) a habitable room should not be an inner room unless

- it has a floor level not more than 4.5 m above ground level and
- it is provided with a door or window for escape or rescue which complies with the provisions of par. 1.5.6;

(ii) all upper floors should be served by a stairway which should

Diagram 9 **Alternative arrangements for escape via the ground storey in dwelling houses with floors more than 4.5 m above ground level** *Par. 1.5.3*

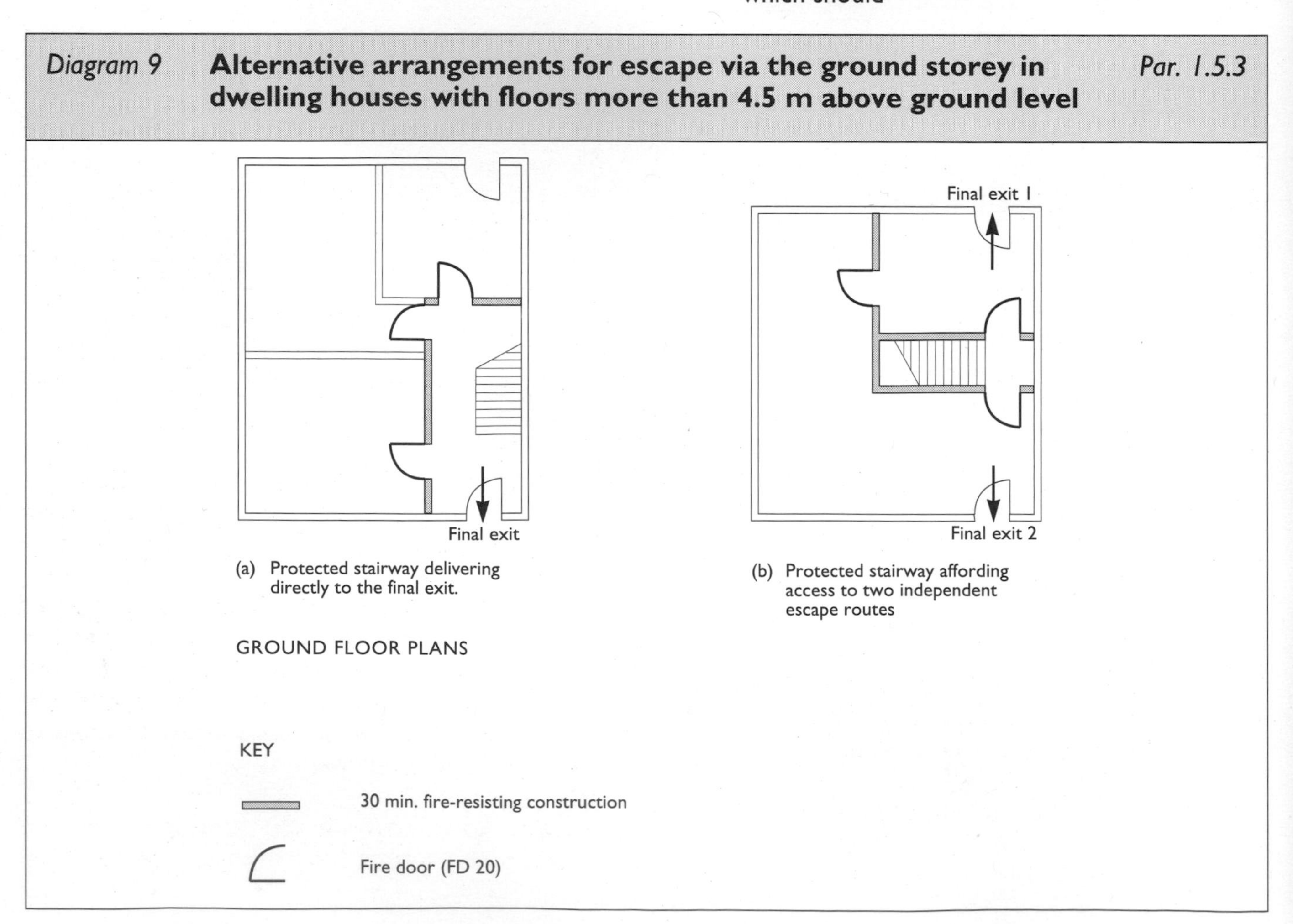

(a) Protected stairway delivering directly to the final exit.

(b) Protected stairway affording access to two independent escape routes

- be a protected stairway (see 1.4.2 and Tables A1, A2);

- connect the ground and all upper storeys; and

- either deliver directly to a final exit (see Diagram 9(a)) or give access to not less than two independent escape routes delivering to alternative final exits (see Diagram 9(b));

(iii) an alternative escape route by way of an escape stairway should be provided from each storey which has a floor 7.5 m or more above the ground or access level. Where the access to the alternative escape route is by way of the protected stairway, the protected stairway at or about 7.5 m above ground or access level should be separated from the lower storeys or levels by fire resisting construction;

(iv) automatic smoke detection and alarms should be provided in accordance with par. 1.5.5; and

(v) the general provisions for dwelling houses, outlined in par. 1.5.8 should be met.

Fire Detection and Alarm Systems for Dwelling Houses

1.5.5 A fire detection and alarm system can significantly increase the level of fire safety in a dwelling house and should be provided in accordance with the following guidance.

BS 5839: Part 6: 1995, Fire detection and alarm systems for buildings, Part 6. Code of practice for the design and installation of fire detection and alarm systems in dwellings, provides guidance on the provision of fire detection and alarm systems in dwellings. This standard refers to different grades and types of fire detection and alarm systems, which can provide varying levels of protection. The grade and system should be selected and installed in accordance with the following paragraphs.

1.5.5.1 Grades of fire detection and alarm systems - The grade of alarm system should be appropriate to the size of the dwelling house, the number of storeys and the fire risk. BS 5839: Part 6: 1995 provides for different grades of systems as follows:

Grade A systems incorporate control and indicating equipment and are designed, installed and maintained in accordance with BS 5839: Part 1: 1988, but with some specific modified provisions.

Grade B systems incorporates fire detectors, fire alarm sounders and control and indicating equipment as specified in BS 5839: Part 6: 1995.

Grade C systems incorporate fire detectors and alarm sounders (which may be combined in the form of smoke alarms) connected to a common power supply with standby supply and an element of central control.

Grade D systems are based on the provision of one or more mains-powered smoke alarms (smoke detector and alarm sounder in a self-contained unit), each provided with an integral standby power supply.

Grade E systems have one or more mains-powered smoke alarms, without a standby power supply.

All smoke alarms for Grade D and E systems should be interconnected so that detection of fire by any one unit provides an audible alarm from each.

The grade of the system should be at least Grade E (and preferably Grade D) as described above. Guidance on the selection of grades of system for other situations, where the fire risk and size of the building so warrants, is contained in BS 5839: Part 6: 1995.

Note: Grade F type systems, which are based on battery-powered smoke alarms, are not acceptable for new dwelling houses.

1.5.5.2 Fire detection and alarm system types - Dwelling houses should be provided with fire detection and alarm systems designed for the protection of life. BS 5839: Part 6: 1995 refers to three levels of protection (system types) intended for this purpose as follows:

An LD1 system incorporates suitably located and interconnected detectors throughout the dwelling house, including all circulation areas that form part of the escape route and in all rooms and areas in which a fire might start, other than toilets, bathrooms and shower rooms.

An LD2 system incorporates suitably located and interconnected detectors in all circulation areas that form part of the escape route and in all rooms or areas, such as kitchens and living rooms, that present a high fire risk.

An LD3 system incorporates suitably located and interconnected detectors in the circulation areas (normally hall-ways, corridors and staircases) that form the escape route. In stairways, alarms are provided at all storey levels. Typically, a two storey dwelling house would have alarms in the hall-way and above the first floor landing. In a typically single-storey dwelling house a single alarm may be adequate. However, if there are long hall-ways or corridors, additional alarms will be necessary.

Dwelling houses with up to three storeys above ground level should have at least an LD3 system. Dwelling houses with more than three storeys, large houses, or where the fire risk so warrants, should be provided with LD2 or LD1 systems as appropriate, which will provide a higher level of life safety. Guidance on system types for different situations is contained in BS 5839: Part 6: 1995.

1.5.5.3 Installation of smoke alarms - Two types of self-contained smoke alarm, an optical type and an ionisation type, which have differing smoke response characteristics, are available. A mixture of both types is recommended and in the case of a typical two storey dwelling house, an optical type on the ground floor storey and an ionisation type on the upper floor may be the most appropriate.

The number and location of smoke alarms will be determined by the system type (see 1.5.5.2). In circulation areas, no door to a habitable room should be further than 7.5 m from the nearest smoke alarm. The location of smoke alarms, particularly in relation to doorways to bedrooms and the spacing of units, should be such as to ensure that the audibility requirements specified in BS 5839: Part 6: 1995 will be achieved.

Smoke alarms should preferably be fixed to the ceiling, at least 300 mm from any wall or light fitting. The method of fixing and location/spacing should take into account instructions provided by the manufacturer of the alarms.

It should be possible to reach all smoke alarms to carry out, easily and safely, routine maintenance such as testing and cleaning. Instructions on maintenance requirements should be provided with all smoke alarm systems.

Windows for Escape or Rescue

1.5.6 Windows may provide an alternative means of escape or may be used for rescue purposes in dwelling houses of limited height. Any window which is required by this sub-section for these purposes should comply with the following:

(a) The window should provide an unobstructed opening not less than 850 mm high and 500 mm wide. The opening section of the window should be secured by means of fastenings which are readily openable from the inside;

(b) The bottom of the window opening should be not more than 1100 mm and not less than 800 mm (600 mm in the case of a rooflight) above the floor of the room in which it is situated;

(c) In the case of a dormer window or roof light, the distance from the eaves of the roof to the cill or vertical plane of the window or cill of the roof-light should not exceed 1.5 m, measured along the roof;

(d) The ground beneath the window should be clear of any obstructions, such as railings or horizontally hung windows, and should be suitable for supporting a ladder safely. The area should be of sufficient size to provide a place of safety from a fire in the house;

(e) A french window or a patio window (doors) should lead to a balcony which is protected with a barrier or railings in accordance with the requirements of Technical Guidance Document K.

Loft Conversions

1.5.7 In the case of an existing two storey dwelling house to which a storey is to be added by converting the existing roof space into habitable accommodation, the following provisions (1.5.7.1 to 1.5.7.7 inclusive) can be applied as an alternative to those in 1.5.3. However, these alternative provisions are not applicable if:

(a) the conversion involves raising the roof-line above the existing ridge, or

(b) the new second storey accommodation exceeds 50 m^2 in area; or

(c) the new second storey is to contain more than two habitable rooms.

In the case of an existing single storey dwelling house to which a storey is to be added by converting the existing roof space into habitable accommodation, the converted dwelling house should comply with the provisions of 1.5.2 above.

1.5.7.1 Enclosure of existing stairway - The Stairway in the ground and first storeys should be enclosed with walls and/or partitions which are fire-resisting, and the enclosure should either:

(a) extend to a final exit (Diagram 9(a)); or

(b) give access to at least two escape routes at ground level, each delivering to final exits and separated from each other by fire-resisting construction and self-closing fire doors (Diagram 9(b)).

1.5.7.2 New stairways - The new storey should be served by a stairway meeting the provisions in Technical Guidance Document K - Stairways, Ramps and Guards. The new stairway should be contained within an enclosure which is formed by extending the existing enclosure in fire resisting construction so that the new accommodation is separated from the existing stairway. Two alternative approaches are given in (a) and (b) below:

(a) The new stairway may rise over the existing stairway and within the same enclosure, in which case the stairway should be separated from the new room(s) by a self-closing fire door set in fire-resisting construction.

(b) The new stairway may alternatively rise from the existing room, in which case the new stairway should be separated from the existing room and the rest of the dwelling house by fire-resisting construction with a self-closing door at the top or bottom of the new stairway.

1.5.7.3 Doorways - All doors to habitable rooms within the enclosure to the existing stairway, should be fitted with a self-closing device. Any new door to a habitable room should be a self-closing fire door (see Appendix B).

1.5.7.4 Glazing - Any glazing in the enclosure to the existing stairway, including glazing in doors (whether or not they need to be fire doors), should be fire-resisting. There should be no openable glazed sections or other ventilation openings in the enclosure to the stairway.

1.5.7.5 Fire Separation of new storey - The new storey should be separated from the rest of the house by fire-resisting construction (see B3, Section 3.1.6). To maintain this separation, measures should be taken to prevent smoke and fire in the stairway from entering the new storey.

1.5.7.6 Escape windows - The room (or rooms) in the new storey should each have an openable window or roof-light for escape or rescue purposes which meets the relevant provisions in 1.5.6 above. The window(s) should also be located to allow suitable pedestrian access for the purpose of rescue by the fire services, or others, by ladder if required.

1.5.7.7 Fire detection and alarm systems - Automatic smoke detection and alarms should be provided throughout the dwelling house in accordance with 1.5.5 above.

General Provisions for Dwelling Houses

1.5.8 The following general provisions apply to dwelling houses.

1.5.8.1 Inner rooms - An inner room is where the access to that room is through another room. A habitable room should not be an inner room unless it is located at basement, ground or first storey and is provided with a window or door suitable for escape or rescue in accordance with the provisions of 1.5.6.

1.5.8.2 Windows for escape or rescue - windows may provide an alternative means of escape or may be used for rescue in dwelling houses. There are specific situations, e.g. as described in paras. 1.5.2, 1.5.3 and 1.5.7.6, where windows in dwelling houses should comply with certain minimum requirements in this regard (see also 1.5.6).

As a general provision, in addition to the specific situations referred to above, all bedrooms in dwelling houses should be provided with windows which comply with the provisions outlined at 1.5.6.

Where windows are being ***replaced*** in existing dwelling houses, it is recommended that bedroom windows should meet, in as far as is practicable, the provisions outlined at 1.5.6. In the case of other habitable rooms, opening sections should not be reduced or altered to an extent that reduces their potential for escape or rescue.

1.5.8.3 Heat producing appliances - Heat Producing appliances include cookers, boilers and open fires which are designed to burn oil, gas or solid fuel. These appliances are a potential source of ignition for fires and it is important that they are correctly installed in dwelling houses. In this regard, critical items include:

- location of the appliance, particularly in relation to escape routes;
- suitable and adequate flues, chimneys fireplaces and hearths as appropriate;
- suitable and adequate ventilation;
- fuel supplies.

Part J of the Second Schedule to the Building Regulations contain requirements in relation to heat producing appliances. Technical Guidance Document J - Heat Producing Appliances, provides guidance on the above items and on how to comply with Part J.

Where a ducted warm air heating system is provided in a dwelling house, precautions should be taken to ensure that it will not contribute to fire spread or endanger the enclosure to any stairway. BS 5588: Part 1: 1990 (Section 6) contains appropriate guidance on these measures.

1.5.8.4 Electrical installations - The electrical installation, comprising wiring, sockets, switches, fuses, distribution board, circuit breakers, earthing, etc., should comply with the National Rules for Electrical Installations produced by the Electro-Technical Council of Ireland.

1.5.8.5 Basements - Basements, where provided in dwelling houses, should be separated from the ground floor storey by means of fire-resisting construction. A stairway serving an upper storey should not extend down to the basement storey.

Any basement habitable room which is an inner room or basement bedroom should be provided with an alternative means of escape.

The fire detection and alarm system (see 1.5.5) should be extended to include any basement areas.

Section B2
Internal Fire Spread (Linings)

Internal fire spread (linings).	**B2**	For the purpose of inhibiting the spread of fire within a building, the internal linings - (a) shall offer adequate resistance to the spread of flame over their surfaces; and (b) shall have, if ignited, a rate of heat release which is reasonable in the circumstances.

Performance

The requirement of B2 may be met if the spread of fire over the internal linings of the building is restricted by making provision for them to have low rates of surface spread of flame and in some cases to have a low rate of heat production, so as to limit the contribution that the fabric of the building makes to fire growth. The extent to which this is necessary is dependent on the location of the lining.

Contents

2.0 Introduction to Provisions

Fire Spread and Lining Materials

2.0.1 The choice of materials for the lining of walls and ceilings can significantly affect the spread of a fire, and its rate of growth, even though they are not likely to be the materials first ignited. This is particularly important in circulation spaces where linings would offer the main vehicle for fire spread, and where rapid spread would be most likely to prevent occupants from escaping.

Two properties of lining materials that are most important in this connection are the rate of flame spread over the surface when it is subject to intense radiant heating, and the rate at which the lining material gives off heat when burning. This Document provides information on how to control internal fire spread through control of these properties.

Floors and Stairways

2.0.2 It is impractical to attempt to control the materials used to cover floors and stairways through Building Regulations, and no provisions are made in this Document about them. Attention is directed however to the provisions of the "Code of Practice for Fire Safety of Furnishings and Fittings in Places of Assembly" published by the Department of the Environment.

Furniture and Fittings

2.0.3 Furniture and fittings can have a major effect on fire spread but it is impractical to attempt to control them through Building Regulations and no provisions are made in this Document about them. Attention is directed however to the provisions of the "Code of Practice for Fire Safety of Furnishings and Fittings in Places of Assembly" and other guides to fire safety in existing buildings published by the Department of the Environment.

Other Controls on Linings Properties

2.0.4 There are provisions for the control of flame spread in two other parts of this Document. In B3 there are provisions in sub-section 3.3 for surfaces exposed in concealed spaces above fire-protecting suspended ceilings, and in sub-section 3.4 for enclosures to above-ground drainage system pipes. In B4, there are provisions in sub-section 4.1 concerning the external surface of walls and in sub-section 4.3 concerning the surface of rooflights in connection with the performance of roof coverings.

Classification of Performance

2.0.5 Appendix A describes the different classes of performance for materials used as a wall or ceiling lining and the appropriate methods of test, including performance ratings for thermoplastic materials, referred to as TP(a) rigid and TP(b). The main classifications used are based on tests in BS 476: Parts 6 and 7. Tests in BS 2782 and BS 5438 are used for classification of thermoplastic materials.

Table A6 of Appendix A gives typical performance ratings which may be achieved by some generic materials and products.

Assessment of Performance

2.0.6 Combustible linings can contribute significantly to the spread of fire in a building and their use should be restricted. The fire performance of lining materials is especially important in circulation spaces and on escape routes. An assessment of the likely performance of lining materials should take account of the following:

- the performance of the lining materials in accordance with the criteria indicated in A7 to A18 of Appendix A,
- the extent and thickness of the lining materials,
- the likely interaction between wall and ceiling linings and between linings and any combustible fittings or fixtures,
- the extent of voids behind the lining materials and the existence of electrical services in such voids.

Care should be taken to ensure that any products which are used to treat lining materials for the purpose of inhibiting spread of flame are applied, and maintained, strictly in accordance with the specification applicable to the relevant test certification supplied by the manufacturer of such products.

Surface treatment of linings is not, in general, a suitable method of achieving Class 0 performance (see A10 of Appendix A). However, in the case of existing lining materials, which satisfy the assessment criteria indicated above, surface treatment to achieve the required performance may be considered.

Care should be taken to ensure that a build up of combustible paints does not reduce the classification of any wall or ceiling lining.

Definitions

2.0.7 The following definitions apply specifically to B2. Other terms applicable more widely throughout the Document are given in Appendix D.

Cavity - Means any space enclosed by the elements of a building (including a suspended ceiling) or contained within an element other than a room, cupboard, circulation space, protected shaft or the space within a flue, chute, duct, pipe or conduit.

Ceiling - A part of a building which encloses and is exposed overhead in a room or circulation space (the soffit of a rooflight is included as part of its surface, but not the frame).

Circulation space - A space (including a protected stairway) mainly used as a means of access between a room and an exit from the building or compartment.

Class 0 - See Appendix A, par. A10.

Rooflight - Any domelight, lantern light, skylight or other element intended to admit daylight through a roof.

Room - An enclosed space in a building that is not an enclosed circulation space (thus the term includes not only conventional rooms, but also cupboards that are not fittings, and large spaces such as warehouses and auditoria).

Thermoplastic material - See Appendix A, par. A14.

Wall - (for the purpose of B2) includes:

(i) the surface of glazing (except glazing in doors), and

(ii) any part of a ceiling which slopes at an angle of 70° or more to the horizontal.

but a wall excludes (for the purpose of B2):

(i) doors and door frames;

(ii) window frames and frames in which glazing is fitted;

(iii) architraves, cover moulds, picture rails, skirtings and similar narrow members; and

(iv) fireplace surrounds, mantle-shelves and fitted furniture.

Provisions meeting the Requirement

2.1 General Provisions

Subject to the variations and specific provisions described in the paragraphs below, the surface linings of walls and ceilings should meet the following classifications -

(a) Class 3 in bathrooms and toilets,

(b) Class 1 in other rooms (except those listed at (e) and (f) below),

(c) Class 1 in circulation spaces within dwellings,

(d) Class 0 in other circulation spaces (including the common areas of flats and maisonettes),

(e) Class 0 in rooms exceeding 30 m^2 in Residential (Institutional) and assembly and recreation buildings, and

(f) Class 0 in places of special fire risk (see 1.0.9).

2.2 Variations and Special Provisions

Walls

2.2.1 Part of the surface of a wall in a room may be of a class lower than specified in 2.1, (but not lower than Class 3) if the area of that part (or, if there are two or more such parts, the total area of those parts) does not exceed, the lesser of the following -

(i) half the floor area of the room, or

(ii) 20 m^2(in the case of a building or compartment of Purpose Group 1, 2 or 5) or 60 m^2 (in any other case); and

In the case of a wall surface in a building of Purpose Group 1, 2, or 5 the area of that part should not exceed 5 m^2 and should be separated from any other such part by a distance of not less than 2 m; or

In the case of a wall surface in a building of any other Purpose Group, the area of that part shall not exceed 15 m^2 and should be separated from any other such part by a distance of not less than 2 m.

Fire-protecting Suspended Ceilings

2.2.2 In addition to satisfying the general provisions set out in 2.1, suspended ceilings that can be accepted as contributing to the fire resistance of a floor must also meet the criteria outlined in paragraph A5 and Table A3 to Appendix A.

Fire-resisting Ceilings

2.2.3 The need for cavity barriers in concealed floor or roof spaces, referred to in sub-section 3.3 of B3, can be reduced by the use of a fire-resisting ceiling below the cavity. Such a ceiling should comply with the following:

(a) it should have at least 30 minute fire resistance;

(b) it should be imperforate except for an opening allowed under par. 3.3.5;

(c) it should extend throughout the building or compartment;

(d) it should not be demountable; and

(e) it should have a Class 0 surface on the soffit, and at least a Class 1 surface facing the cavity.

2.3 Thermoplastic Materials

2.3.1 Thermoplastic materials (see Appendix A, pars. A14, A15) which cannot meet the performance specified in paragraph 2.1 can be used in windows, rooflights and lighting diffusers in ceilings if they comply with the provisions of the following paragraphs:

Windows

2.3.2 External windows to rooms (though not to circulation spaces) may be glazed with thermoplastic materials, if the material can be classified as a TP(a) rigid product.

Internal glazing should meet the provisions in par. 2.1 above. Note that a wall does not include glazing in a door.

Rooflights

2.3.3 Rooflights to rooms and circulation spaces (with the exception of protected stairways) may be constructed of a thermoplastic material if:

(a) the lower surface has a TP(a) (rigid) or TP(b) classification (see A14, Appendix A)

(b) the size and disposition of the rooflights accords with the limitations in Table 2.1, Diagram 10 and Table 4.5 to Section B4.

Lighting Diffusers

2.3.4 Lighting diffusers are translucent or open-structured elements that allow light to pass through. They may be part of a luminaire or used below rooflights or other sources of light. The following provisions apply only to lighting diffusers which form part of a ceiling and are not concerned with diffusers of light fittings which are attached to the soffit of, or suspended beneath a ceiling

Thermoplastic lighting diffusers should not be used in fire protecting or fire resisting ceilings, unless they have been satisfactorily tested as part of the ceiling system that is to be used to provide the appropriate fire protection.

Ceilings to rooms and circulation spaces (but not protected stairways) may incorporate thermoplastic lighting diffusers if the following provisions are observed:-

(a) Wall and ceiling surfaces exposed within the space above the suspended ceiling (other than the upper surfaces of the thermoplastic panels) should comply with the general provisions of par. 2.1, according to the type of space below the suspended ceiling.

(b) If the diffusers are of classification TP(a) (rigid), there are no restrictions on their extent.

(c) If the diffusers are of classification TP(b), they should be limited in extent as indicated in Table 2.1 and Diagram 10.

Thermoplastic materials which have a lesser performance than TP(b) should not be used for lighting diffusers which form part of a ceiling.

Table 2.1 **Limitations applied to thermoplastic lighting diffusers in suspended ceilings and thermoplastic rooflights**

Minimum classification of lower surface	Use of space below the diffusers or rooflight	Maximum area of each diffuser panel or rooflight [1]	Max total area of diffuser panels and rooflights as percentage of floor area of the space in which the ceiling is located	Minimum distance between diffuser panels or rooflights [1]
TP(a) Rigid	any except protected stairway	No Limit	No Limit	No Limit
TP(b)	rooms	5 sq.m	50	3 m
	circulation spaces except protected stairways	5 sq.m	15	3 m

Note:

1. Smaller panels can be grouped together provided that the overall size of the group and the space between one group and any others satisfies the dimensions shown in Diagram 10.

Layout restrictions on TP(b) thermoplastic lighting diffusers and rooflights

Par. 2.3.3, Table 2.1

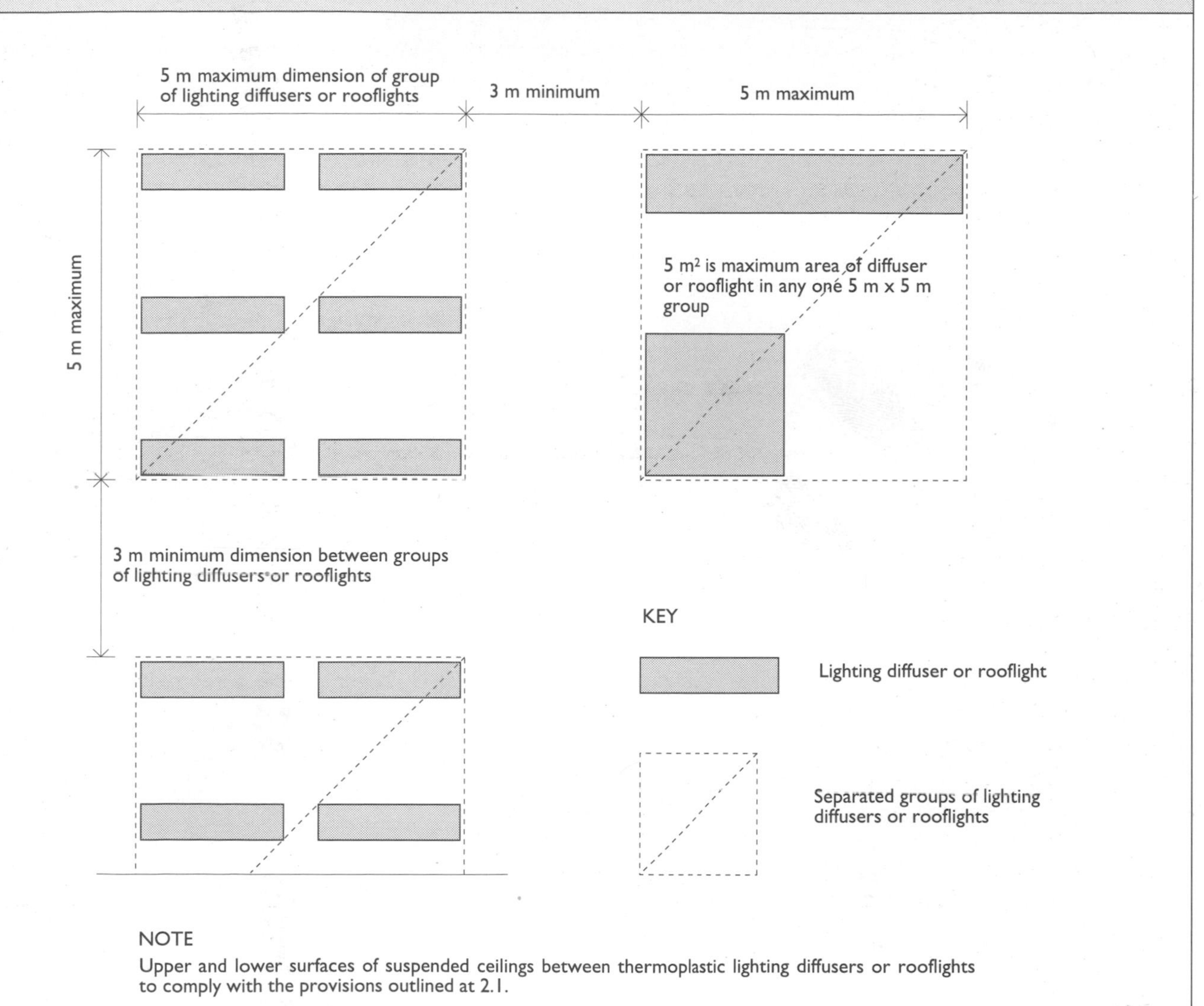

NOTE

Upper and lower surfaces of suspended ceilings between thermoplastic lighting diffusers or rooflights to comply with the provisions outlined at 2.1.

Section B3
Internal Fire Spread (Structure)

Internal fire spread (structure). **B3**	(1)	A building shall be so designed and constructed that, in the event of fire, its stability will be maintained for a reasonable period.
	(2)	(a) A wall common to two or more buildings shall be so designed and constructed that it offers adequate resistance to the spread of fire between those buildings.
		(b) A building shall be sub-divided with fire resisting construction where this is necessary to inhibit the spread of fire within the building.
	(3)	A building shall be so designed and constructed that the unseen spread of fire and smoke within concealed spaces in its structure or fabric is inhibited where necessary.
	(4)	For the purposes of sub-paragraph 2(a), a house in a terrace and a semi-detached house are each to be treated as being a separate building.

Performance

The requirements of B3 may be met:

(a) if the structural elements of the building are capable of withstanding the effects of fire for an appropriate period without loss of stability,

(b) if the building is sub-divided by elements of fire-resisting construction into compartments,

(c) if any openings in fire separating elements are suitably protected in order to maintain the fire integrity of the element, and

(d) if any hidden voids in the construction are sealed and subdivided to inhibit the unseen spread of fire and products of combustion, in order to reduce the risk of structural failure and the spread of fire, in so far as they pose a threat to the safety of people in and around the building.

The extent to which any of these measures are necessary is dependent on the use of the building and, in some cases its size, and on the location of the element of construction.

Contents

3.0 Introduction to Provisions

3.0.1 Provisions for loadbearing elements of structure are given in sub-section 3.1. Sub-section 3.2 is concerned with the subdivision of a building into compartments, and sub-section 3.3 makes provisions about concealed spaces (or cavities). Sub-section 3.4 gives information on the protection of openings and on fire-stopping which relates to compartmentation and to fire spread in concealed spaces. Sub-section 3.5 is concerned with special provisions which apply to certain types of buildings. Common to all these sub-sections and to other provisions of this Document is the property of fire resistance.

Fire Resistance

3.0.2 The fire resistance of an element of construction is a measure of its ability to withstand the effects of fire in one or more ways:

- resistance to collapse, i.e. the ability to maintain loadbearing capacity (which applies to loadbearing members only);

- resistance to fire penetration, i.e. an ability to maintain the integrity of the element (which applies to fire-separating elements);

- resistance to the transfer of excessive heat, i.e. an ability to provide insulation from high temperatures (which applies to fire-separating elements).

Provisions Elsewhere in Technical Guidance Document B concerning Fire Resistance

3.0.3 There are provisions in Section B1 concerning the use of fire-resisting construction to protect means of escape.

There are provisions in Section B4 for fire resistance of external walls to restrict the spread of fire between buildings.

There are provisions in Section B5 for fire resistance in the construction of fire-fighting shafts.

Appendix A gives information on methods of test and performance for elements of construction.

Appendix B gives information on fire-resisting doors.

Material Alteration

3.0.4 In the case of a material alteration of a building and where a material change of use of the building is not also involved, the provisions in relation to the fire resistance for loadbearing elements of Structure (See 3.1) contained in any Guide or Code of Practice, published by the Department of the Environment for the purpose of section 18(2) of the Fire Services Act, 1981, for the type of premises to which the material alteration is carried out, may be used as an alternative to the relevant provisions of this Technical Guidance Document.

Definitions

3.0.5 The following definitions apply specifically to Section B3. Other terms applicable more widely throughout this Document are given in Appendix D.

Appliance ventilation duct - A duct provided to convey combustion air to a gas appliance.

Cavity barrier - A construction provided to close a concealed space against penetration of smoke or flame, or provided to restrict the movement of smoke or flame within such a space.

Concealed space (cavity) - A space enclosed by elements of a building (including a suspended ceiling) or contained within an element, but not a room, cupboard, circulation space, protected shaft or space within a flue, chute, duct, pipe or conduit.

Compartment - A building or part of a building, comprising one or more rooms, spaces or storeys, constructed to prevent the spread of fire to or from another part of the same building, or an adjoining building.

Compartment wall or floor - A fire-resisting wall or floor used in the separation of one fire compartment from another.

Fire stop - A seal provided to close an imperfection of fit or design tolerance between elements or components, to restrict or prevent the passage of fire and smoke.

Pipe - Includes: pipe fittings and accessories; excludes: a flue pipe and a pipe used for ventilating purposes (other than a ventilating pipe for an above ground drainage system).

Platform floor (access or raised floor) - A floor supported by a structural floor, but with an intervening concealed space which is intended to house services.

Separating wall - A compartment wall used to separate one building from another, which is the full height of the buildings and is in a continuous vertical plane.

Provisions meeting the Requirement

3.1 Loadbearing Elements of Structure

Introduction

3.1.1 Premature failure of the structure can be prevented by provision for loadbearing elements of structure to have a minimum standard of fire resistance, in terms of resistance to collapse or failure of loadbearing capacity.

The purpose in providing the structure with fire resistance is threefold:

- to protect the occupants, some of whom may have to remain in the building for some time while evacuation proceeds, if the building is a large one;

- to protect fire fighters who may be engaged in search or rescue operations (though this is limited and is not intended to cover fire-fighting operations generally);

- to reduce the danger to people in the vicinity of the building who might be hurt by falling debris or by the impact of the collapsing structure on other buildings.

Fire Resistance Standard

3.1.2 Structural frames, beams, columns, loadbearing walls (internal and external), floor structures and gallery structures, should have at least the fire resistance given in Appendix A, Table A1.

Application of the Fire Resistance Standards for Loadbearing Elements
(see Appendix A, Tables A1 and A2)

3.1.3 The measures set out in Appendix A include provisions to ensure that where one element of structure supports or gives stability to another element of structure, the supporting element has no less fire resistance than the other element.

The measures also provide for elements of structure that are common to more than one building or compartment, to be constructed to the standard of the greater of the relevant provisions. Special provisions about fire resistance of elements of structure in single storey buildings are also given, and there are concessions in respect of fire resistance of elements of structure in basements where at least one side of the basement is open at ground level. See "Application of the fire resistance standard in Table A2" in Appendix A.

Exclusions from the Provisions for Elements of Structure

3.1.4 The following are excluded from the definition of elements of structure for the purposes of these provisions:

(a) a structure that only supports a roof, unless the roof performs the function of a floor, e.g. for parking vehicles, or as a means of escape (see B1) or is essential for the stability of an external wall which is required to have fire resistance (see B4);

(b) the lowest floor of the building; and

(c) a platform floor.

Additional Provisions

3.1.5 Additional provisions are required if a loadbearing wall is also -

(a) a compartment wall (see 3.2);

(b) a wall between a house and a small garage (see 3.2, par. 3.2.4.2);

(c) protecting a means of escape (see B1, par. 1.4.2);

(d) an external wall (see B4, sub-section 4.1 and 4.2);

(e) enclosing a firefighting shaft (see B5, sub-section 5.3).

If a floor is also a compartment floor, see sub-section 3.2.

Floors in Domestic Loft Conversions

3.1.6 In altering an existing two storey single dwelling house to provide additional storeys, the floor(s), both old and new, should have the full 30 minute standard of fire resistance shown in Appendix A, Table A1. However, where only one

Building Regulations, 1997
Addenda et Corrigenda
Amendment to Technical Guidance Documents (1997)

The section entitled **"Transitional Arrangements"** in Page 2 of each of the Technical Guidance Documents is amended as follows:-

4th line: Replace the "1 January, 1998" with "1 July, 1998".

11th line: Replace the "1 January, 1998" with "1 July, 1998".

(b) the number of persons likely to be on the floor at any one time is low and does not include members of the public;

(c) the layout is such that any persons on the floor would be readily aware of any fire starting at the lower level; and

(d) at least one stairway serving the raised floors, platform or tier discharges within 3 m of an exit from the building.

Features of layout or design that would allow occupants to be aware of a fire starting at the lower level include the use of perforations in the floor of the structure, or leaving a space between the edge of the platform and the walls of the room housing it, to make the smoke and the sounds of the fire obvious. If the floor is more than 10 m in width or length, an automatic fire detection and alarm system should be used to provide sufficiently early warning.

3.2 Compartmentation

Introduction

3.2.1 The spread of fire within a building can be restricted by sub-dividing it into compartments separated from one another by walls and/or floors of fire-resisting construction. The object is twofold:

(a) to prevent rapid fire spread which could trap occupants of the building; and

(b) to reduce the chance of fires becoming large, on the basis that large fires are more dangerous, not only to occupants but to people in the vicinity of the building.

Compartmentation is complementary to provisions made under Section B1 for the protection of escape routes, and to provisions made under Section B4 against the spread of fire between buildings.

The degree of sub-division that is appropriate depends on:

(a) the use of the building, which affects the potential for fires and the severity of fires, as well as the ease of evacuation;

(b) the height of the top storey in the building, which is an indication of the ease of evacuation and the ability of the fire service to intervene effectively; and

(c) the availability of a fire suppression system which affects the growth rate of the fire, and may suppress it altogether.

Forms of Compartmentation

3.2.2 Sub-division is achieved using compartment walls and compartment floors, and provisions for their construction are given in pars. 3.2.5 et seq. These construction provisions vary according to the function of the wall or floor.

Special forms of compartmentation to which particular construction provisions apply, are:

(a) walls common to two or more buildings (separating wall);

(b) walls dividing buildings into separated parts (in which the parts can be assessed independently for the purpose of determining the appropriate standard of fire resistance); and

(c) walls protecting houses from attached or integral small garages.

Junctions and Protected Shafts

3.2.3 For compartmentation to be effective, there should be continuity at the junctions of the fire-resisting elements enclosing a compartment, and any openings from one compartment to another should not present a weakness.

Spaces that connect compartments, such as stairways and service shafts, need to be protected to restrict fire spread between the compartments, and they are termed protected shafts.

Provision of Compartment Walls and Compartment Floors

3.2.4 Compartment walls and compartment floors should be provided in the circumstances described in pars. 3.2.4.1 to 3.2.4.7 below, with the provision that the lowest floor in a building does not need to be constructed as a compartment floor.

Provisions for the construction of compartment walls and compartment floors in different circumstances are given in 3.2.5.

Provisions for the protection of openings in compartment walls and compartment floors are given in 3.2.6 and 3.2.7.

Diagram 11 illustrates schematically various forms of compartmentation and indicates the paragraph references for the relevant guidance.

3.2.4.1 All purpose groups - The following guidance applies to all buildings and all purpose groups:

(a) A wall common to two or more buildings (separating wall) should be constructed as a compartment wall;

Diagram 11 **Compartment walls and compartment floors** *Par. 3.2.4*

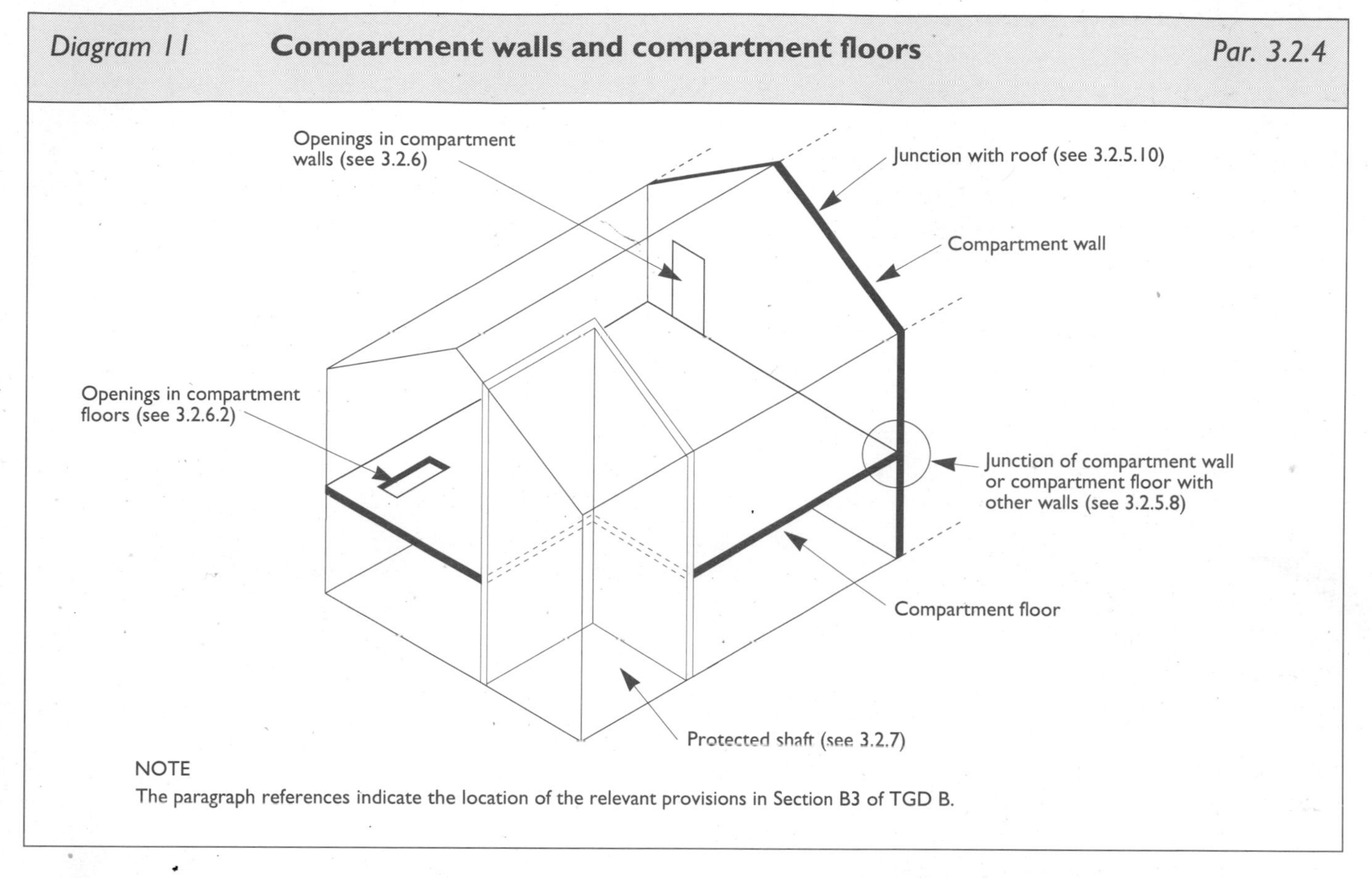

NOTE
The paragraph references indicate the location of the relevant provisions in Section B3 of TGD B.

(b) Compartment walls and/or compartment floors should be provided to separate parts of a building that are occupied mainly for different purposes (see 0.3.2 and Table 0.1), or by different tenancies, from one another;

(c) Where part of a building is used for a purpose that is ancillary to another purpose (see 0.3.2), it need not be separated by compartment walls and/or floors, unless that part is a place of special fire risk (see 1.0.9);

(d) Compartment walls and/or floors should be provided to separate places of special fire risk (see 1.0.9) from other parts of a building.

Note: Many of the codes of practice and other documents referred to in Section B1 (1.1) for the purpose of the means of escape, identify specific areas of ancillary accommodation that are regarded as places of special fire risk. These areas should also be separated by way of compartmentation in accordance with the recommendations contained in those documents.

3.2.4.2 Dwelling houses - Any wall separating semi-detached dwelling houses, or houses in a terrace, should be constructed as a compartment wall, and the dwelling houses should be considered as separate buildings.

If a small garage is attached to (or forms part of) a dwelling house, the garage should be separated from the rest of the house as indicated in Diagram 12.

3.2.4.3 Flats and maisonettes - In buildings containing flats (purpose group 1(c)) the following should be constructed as compartment walls or compartment floors:

(a) any floor (unless it is within a maisonette, i.e. between one storey and another within one dwelling), and

(b) any wall separating a flat from any other part of the building, and

(c) any wall enclosing a refuse storage chamber.

Diagram 12 **Separation between garage and dwelling house** *Par. 3.2.4.2*

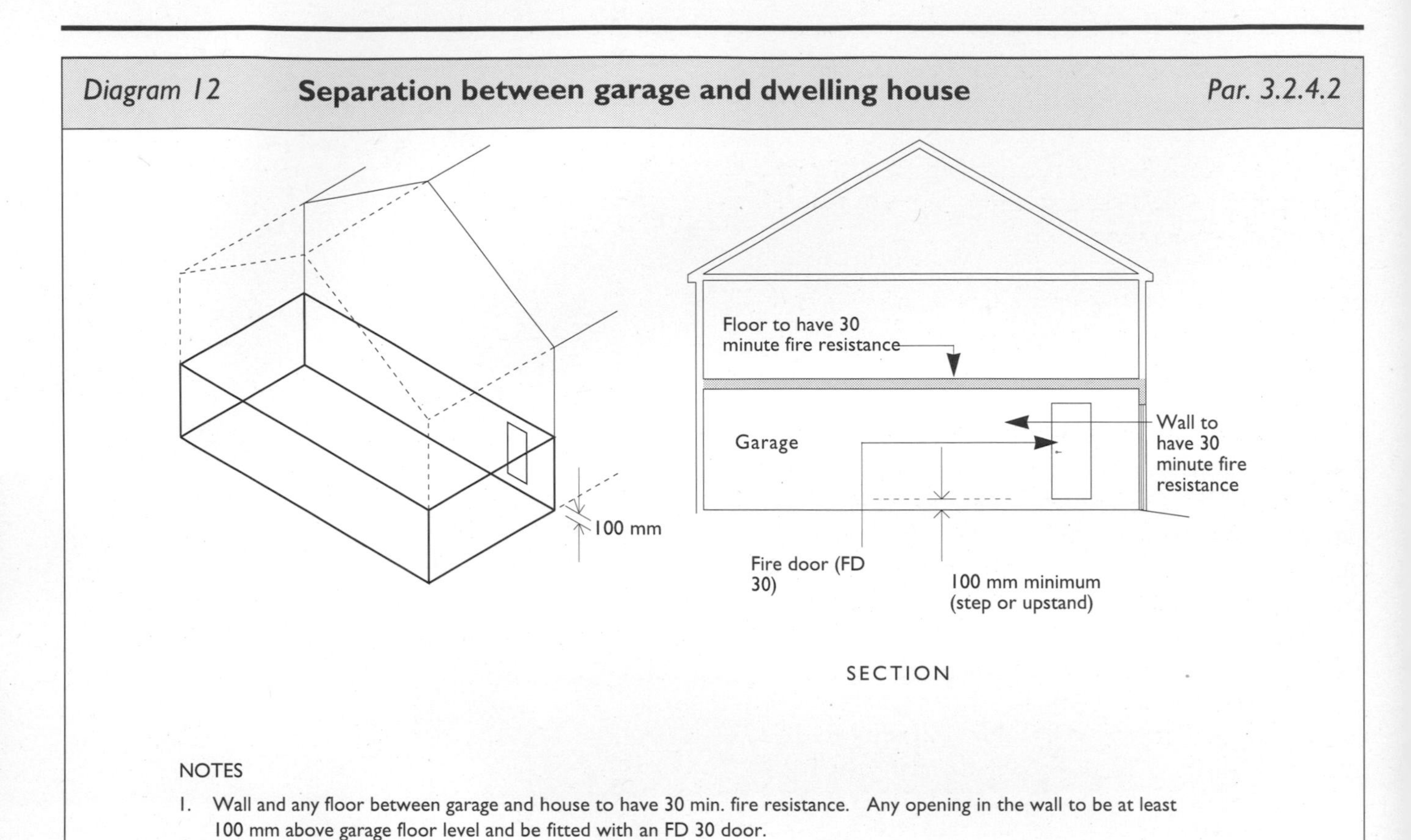

NOTES

1. Wall and any floor between garage and house to have 30 min. fire resistance. Any opening in the wall to be at least 100 mm above garage floor level and be fitted with an FD 30 door.

2. In the case of a single storey house, in order to maintain a 30 minute standard of fire separation between the house and the garage, either:
   the wall between the house and the garage should be taken up to the underside of the roof, or
   the ceiling to the garage should be made fire-resisting.

3.2.4.4 Residential (Institutional) buildings - The following walls and floors should be constructed as compartment walls and compartment floors in Residential (Institutional) buildings (Purpose Group 2(a)):

(a) any floor, other than the floor of the lowest storey;

(b) any wall needed to sub-divide a storey to observe the limits for compartment sizes outlined in Table 3.1;

(c) any wall needed to sub-divide a storey into at least two compartments for the purpose of progressive horizontal evacuation (see 1.2.7).

3.2.4.5 Other residential buildings - The following walls and floors should be constructed as compartment walls and compartment floors in Other Residential buildings (Purpose Group 2(b)):

(a) any floor, other than the floor of the lowest storey;

(b) any wall needed to sub-divide a storey to observe the limits for compartment sizes outlined in Table 3.1.

3.2.4.6 Non-residential buildings - The following walls and floors should be constructed as compartment walls and compartment floors in buildings of a non-residential purpose group (i.e. Office, Shop, Shopping centre, Assembly & Recreation, Industrial, Storage or Other Non-Residential):

(a) any wall/floor needed to sub-divide the building to observe the size limits on compartments given in Table 3.1;

(b) any floor if the building, or separated part of the building, has a storey with a floor at a height of more than 30 m above ground level;

(c) the floor of the ground storey if the building has one or more basements;

(d) any basement floor if the building, or separated part, has a basement at a depth of more than 10 m below ground level; and

(e) in the case of a shopping centre, any walls or floors required to comply with the provisions outlined in 3.2.4.7 below.

3.2.4.7 Shopping centres (Purpose Group 4(b)) - Shopping centres require special provisions in relation to compartmentation, because of the nature of the occupancies and the arrangement of individual units that make up these buildings and the fact that enclosed pedestrian mall areas are generally provided between individual units. While the majority of units comprise of individual shops of varying sizes, other uses such as assembly and recreation or offices may also be provided in these buildings. In addition, certain ancillary accommodation, such as service and storage areas present particular high fire risk and require compartmentation.

Compartmentation in shopping complexes should comply with the recommendations outlined in section 5 of BS 5588 Fire precautions in the design, construction and use of buildings, Part 10 Code of practice for shopping complexes.

Special provisions relating to shopping centres generally, concerning structural fire protection, are outlined in 3.5.3.

Table 3.1 Maximum area and cubic capacity of a building or compartment

Use	Purpose Group	Building form	Maximum floor area (1) of any one storey in the building or compartment (m^2)	Maximum cubic capacity(1) of building or compartment (m^3)
Residential (Dwellings)	1(a) 1(b) 1(c)	any	no limit	no limit
Residential (Institutional)	2(a)	single storey more than one storey	3000 (3) 1500 (3)	no limit (3) no limit (3)
Other Residential	2(b)	more than one storey	2000 (3)	no limit (3)
Office	3	more than one storey	4600	28000
Shop	4(a)	single storey more than one storey	4000 2800	20000 7100
Shopping Centre	4(b)	any	see 3.5.3	see 3.5.3
Assembly and Recreation, Other Non-Residential	5, 8	more than one storey	1900	21000
Industrial (2)	6	single storey (a) normal hazard (b) high hazard	 93000 33000	 no limit no limit
		more than one storey (a) normal hazard (b) high hazard	 7500 2800	 no limit 17000
Storage (2)	7(a)	single storey (a) normal hazard (b) high hazard	 14000 1000	 no limit no limit
		more than one storey (a) normal hazard (b) high hazard	 2800 500	 21000 4200
	7(b)	car park	no limit	no limit

Notes:

1. Other factors may also determine the provision of compartment walls and floors (see 3.2.4). For buildings of any purpose groups, other than 2(a) and 2(b), these figures may be doubled if the building is provided throughout with an appropriate automatic sprinkler system meeting the relevant recommendations of BS 5306: Part 2: 1990 Fire extinguishing installations and equipment on premises, Part 2 Specification for sprinkler systems, i.e. the relevant occupancy rating together with additional requirements for life safety.

2. See Appendix E for guidance on assessment of risk in Industrial and Storage buildings.

3. In buildings of Purpose Groups 2(a) and 2(b), all floors other than the lowest floor are constructed as compartment floors (see 3.2.4.4 and 3.2.4.5). In these cases the maximum area of compartment is the limiting factor.

Construction of Compartment Floors and Compartment Walls

3.2.5 Every compartment wall and compartment floor should:

(a) form a complete barrier to fire between the compartments they separate;

(b) have the appropriate fire resistance as indicated in Appendix A, Tables A1 and A2; and

(c) be constructed in accordance with the relevant guidance in the following pars. 3.2.5.1 to 3.2.5.10.

The performance requirements for fire resisting elements of construction are indicated in Appendix A, paragraph A5.

3.2.5.1 Compartment floors in residential (Institutional) buildings - In a building of Purpose Group 2(a), Residential (Institutional), all compartment floors should be constructed of non-combustible materials (see Appendix A, Table A8).

An exception to the requirement for non-combustible compartment floors may be made in the case of a material alteration of an existing Residential (Institutional) building.

3.2.5.2 Compartment floors in high buildings - In a building of any purpose group, where the height of the top storey is 10 m or more (see Appendix C, Diagram 38), any compartment floor which is required to have a fire resistance of 60 minutes of more should be constructed of non-combustible materials (see Appendix A, Table A8), apart from any floor finish.

An exception to the requirement for non-combustible compartment floors may be made in the case of an existing floor in an existing building used for any purpose other than Residential (Institutional), Purpose Group 2(a).

Note: The non-combustibility requirement does not apply in the case of a material alteration of an existing Residential (Institutional) building (see 3.2.5.1).

3.2.5.3 Fire resistance of timber floors in existing buildings - In an existing building it may be possible to increase the fire resistance of existing timber floors. The techniques generally adopted to upgrade the fire resistance of timber floors are as follows:

(a) The addition of a fire-resisting layer, or layers, beneath the existing floor joists. There are many techniques and materials available for such purposes. In some cases it is also necessary to provide a protective layer on top of the existing floor-boards or between the floor joists.

(b) Filling the voids between the existing floor surface and ceiling below, or between the floor joists, with a suitable material. There are a number of proprietary systems available which are based on this method. These are often more appropriate than the method outlined at (a) above in buildings of historic or architectural interest, where existing plasterwork is to be retained.

Many of the techniques employed in upgrading timber floors involve the use of proprietary materials and systems. These must be capable of achieving the required performance in the situations for which they are adopted. Particular care and attention to detail in the execution of any such upgrading works is necessary to ensure the required performance.

Table 14 of Building Research Establishment Report "Guidelines for the construction of fire-resisting structural elements (BR 128, 1988)" provides guidance in relation to the construction of fire-resisting timber floors. Guidance on fire-resisting timber floors is also available from the Timber Research and Development Association (TRADA) and in the trade literature produced by manufacturers of fire protection materials and products.

Guidance on upgrading the fire resistance of existing timber floors is provided in Building Research Digest number 208 "Increasing the fire resistance of existing timber floors (revised 1988)".

3.2.5.4 Compartment walls - In a building of purpose group 2(a), Residential (Institutional) and in a building of any purpose group, where the height of the top storey is 10 m or more (see Appendix C, Diagram 38), a compartment wall which is required to have a fire resistance of one hour or more should be constructed of materials of limited combustibility (see Appendix A, Table A7), apart from any wall surface complying with the requirements of B2, internal fire spread (linings).

3.2.5.5 Separating walls - Compartment walls that are common to two or more buildings (separating walls) should run the full height of the building in a continuous vertical plane and should be constructed of non-combustible (see Appendix A, Table A8) materials. Adjoining buildings should only be separated by walls, not floors. A compartment wall being used to divide a building into separate occupancies or uses would not be subject to this provision.

3.2.5.6 Separating walls in dwelling houses - An exception to the requirement for separating walls to be constructed of non-combustible materials may be permitted in the case of a separating wall between buildings of Purpose Group 1(a) Residential (Dwellings) of one or two storeys only, where the wall is part of a timber frame construction system consisting only of a structural frame of combustible materials, and containing no pipes, wires or other services, and the design, materials and workmanship used in the manufacture and construction of the wall are in accordance with the provisions of Technical Guidance Document D.

3.2.5.7 Separated parts - Compartment walls used to form a separated part of a building (see 3.2.2 (b)) should run the full height of the building in a continuous vertical plane.

3.2.5.8 Junction of compartment wall or compartment floor with other walls - Where a compartment wall or compartment floor meets another compartment wall, or an external wall, the junction should maintain the fire resistance of the compartmentation.

There are provisions in Section B1 in relation to the junction of an external wall and the enclosure to a protected stairway (see 1.3.6.6).

Consideration may also be required in the case of junctions of compartment walls and re-entrant or opposing elevations of the same building (see 3.2.5.9).

3.2.5.9 Courtyards, light-wells and opposite elevations of the same building - In the case of buildings which contains courtyards, light-wells or wings, the unprotected areas on opposing or adjacent elevations could contribute to the transfer of fire between compartments. An important area in this respect is where a compartment wall meets at the junction formed by the internal angle of two elevations to a building. In this situation, the external walls should be protected on one or both elevations for a sufficient distance to limit the potential for horizontal fire spread between the compartments. In other situations, to limit fire spread between different compartments, it may be necessary to consider the space separation between opposing elevations.

In the case a Residential (Institutional) building, where the means of escape (see Section B1) have been designed on the basis of progressive horizontal evacuation, special consideration is required for the junctions between compartment walls and the external elevations of the building (see 3.5.4).

3.2.5.10 Junction of compartment wall and roof - The junction between a compartment wall and the roof of a building should be capable of restricting fire spread between compartments. A compartment wall should be taken up to meet the underside of the roof covering or deck and fire stopped where necessary at the wall/roof junction.

A compartment wall should not be stopped at ceiling level while using a cavity barrier in the roof space to continue the line of compartment to the roof. The construction of the wall, particularly between any ceiling and the roof, should not contain imperfections that would provide a route for fire penetration or premature failure of the fire resistance performance of the wall. The gap between the wall and the underside of the roof should be as small as practicable (generally not greater than 50 mm) and be filled with suitable fire stopping material over the full width of the wall.

Where structural roof members such as beams, purlins and rafters are built into or carried across a masonry or concrete compartment wall, any openings for them should be as small as practicable and any gaps should be effectively fire stopped with non-combustible fire stopping material over the full width of the wall. Where a trussed rafter supporting a roof is carried across a compartment wall it should be designed so that failure due to fire in one compartment will not cause failure of any part of the truss in another compartment.

The design and detailing of the junction between a compartment wall and any roof valley, gutter or other roof configuration, should be carefully considered so as to ensure that a means is not provided at the junction for premature fire spread between compartments.

If a fire penetrates a roof near a compartment wall there is a risk that it will spread over the roof to the adjoining compartment. To reduce that risk, the junction between a compartment wall and a roof should be constructed in accordance with the following:

(a) a zone of the roof at least 1.5 m wide on both sides of the wall should have a covering of designation AA, AB and AC (see Table A5 to Appendix A) on a non-combustible (see Table A8 to Appendix A) sub-strata or deck. The compartment wall should be carried up to the underside of the roof deck and be fire stopped with resilient non-combustible fire stopping material over the full width of the wall (see Diagram 13(A)).

    Note: where the roof deck comprises a double-skin insulated sheet, the insulating material directly above the compartment wall should be of limited combustibility (see A16 and Table A7 of Appendix A) for a width of not less than 300 mm which forms a fire stopping seal to the cavity between the inner and outer skins. In the case of a non-insulated double skin roof deck, similar fire stopping should also be provided.

(b) in buildings not more than 15 m high (see Diagram 37, Appendix C) which are used as offices, assembly and recreation or as dwellings, timber tiling battens or combustible boarding not exceeding 25 mm in thickness used as a substrate to the roof covering may be carried over the compartment wall, provided that they are fully bedded in mortar or other suitable non-combustible fire stopping material for the full width of the wall, and any cavities within the thickness of the roof, above and below the sarking felt or similar membrane along the line of the wall and at the eaves are adequately fire stopped (see Diagram 13(B)).

(c) As an alternative to (a) or (b) above the compartment wall may be extended above the line of the external roof surface by a height of not less than 375 mm to form a parapet wall (see Diagram 13(C)).

(d) As an alternative to (a), (b) or (c) above for any building type, any other system which has been shown by test to be equally effective in restricting the spread of fire at a compartment wall/roof junction may be used.

Diagram 13 Junction of compartment wall with roof *Par. 3.2.5.10*

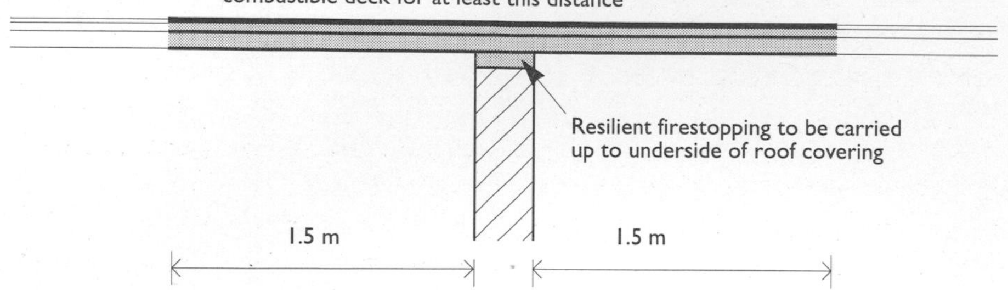

A. BUILDING OR COMPARTMENT AT ANY HEIGHT AND USE

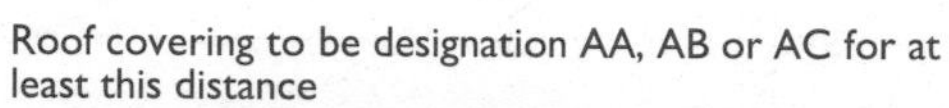

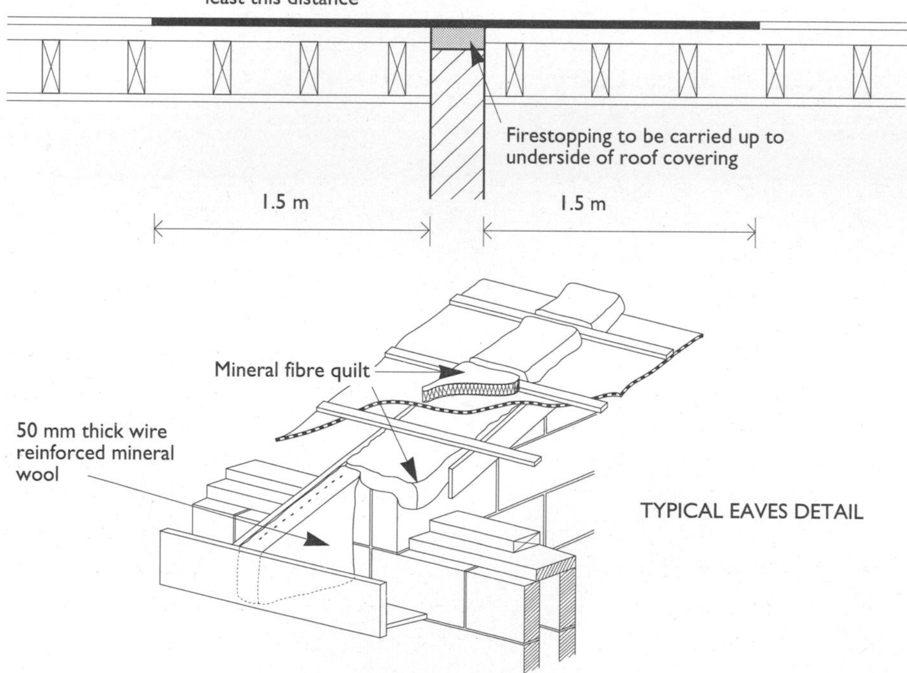

Boarding (used as a substrate), woodwool slabs or timber tiling battens may be carried over the wall provided that they are fully bedded in mortar (or other non-combustible fire stopping material)

B. DWELLING HOUSE AND BUILDING OR COMPARTMENT IN RESIDENTIAL (EXCEPT INSTITUTIONAL), OFFICE, OR ASSEMBLY USE NOT MORE THAN 15 m HIGH

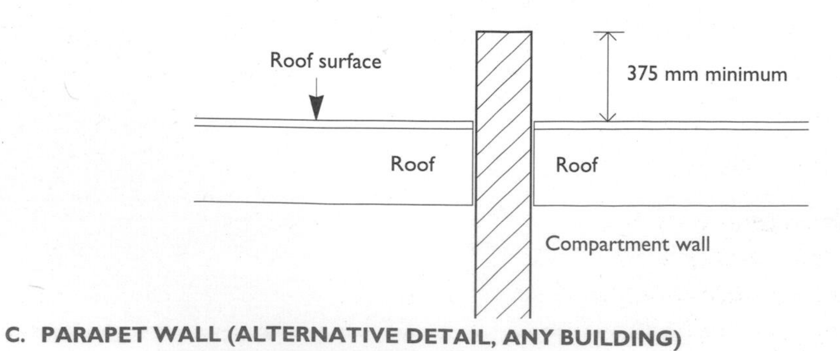

C. PARAPET WALL (ALTERNATIVE DETAIL, ANY BUILDING)

Openings Between Compartments

3.2.6 Any door openings in compartment walls should be protected by means of fire doors, in accordance with the provisions outlined in Appendix B and Table B1. Openings for the passage of pipes, ducts and other services should be protected in accordance with the provisions outlined in sub-section 3.4.

3.2.6.1 Openings in separating walls - Any openings in a wall which is common to two or more buildings should be limited to those for:

(a) a door which is needed to provide a means of escape in case of fire and which has the same fire resistance as that required for the wall (see Appendix B, Table B1) and is fitted in accordance with the provisions of Appendix B; and

(b) the passage of a pipe which meets the provisions in Section 3.4.

3.2.6.2 Openings in other compartment walls or in compartment floors - Openings in compartment walls (other than those described in par. 3.2.6.1) or compartment floors should be limited to those for:

(a) doors which have the appropriate fire resistance given in Appendix B, Table B1, and are fitted in accordance with the provisions of Appendix B; and

(b) the passage of pipes, ventilation ducts, chimneys, appliance ventilation ducts or ducts encasing one or more flue pipes, which meet the provisions in sub-section 3.4; and

(c) refuse chutes of non-combustible construction; and

(d) protected shafts which meet the relevant provisions below.

Protected Shafts

3.2.7 Any stairway or other shaft passing directly from one compartment to another, should be enclosed so as to delay or prevent the spread of fire between compartments, and is termed a protected shaft.

If the protected shaft is a stairway, see also B1 for provisions relating to protected stairways and B5 if the stairway also serves as a fire-fighting stairway.

3.2.7.1 Construction of protected shafts - The construction enclosing a protected shaft (see Diagram 14) should:

(a) form a complete barrier to fire between the different compartments which the shaft connects;

(b) have the appropriate fire resistance given in Appendix A, Table A1, except for glazed screens which meet the provisions of par. 3.2.7.3;

(c) meet the requirements of section 3.2.5 for the construction of compartment walls; and

(d) satisfy the provisions about their use, ventilation and the treatment of openings in the paragraphs below.

3.2.7.2 Use for protected shafts - The uses of protected shafts should be restricted to stairways, lifts, escalators, chutes, ducts, pipes, and/or as sanitary accommodation and washrooms.

3.2.7.3 Glazed screens to protected shafts - Where a protected shaft contains a stairway, but is not a fire-fighting shaft (see B5), and is entered from a protected corridor or lobby, the part of the enclosure between the shaft and the corridor or lobby may incorporate glass so as to provide at least 30 minutes fire resistance in terms of integrity only, if the principles in Diagram 15 and the provisions of Table A4 of Appendix A are met.

Diagram 14 **Protected shafts (construction)** *Par. 3.2.7.1*

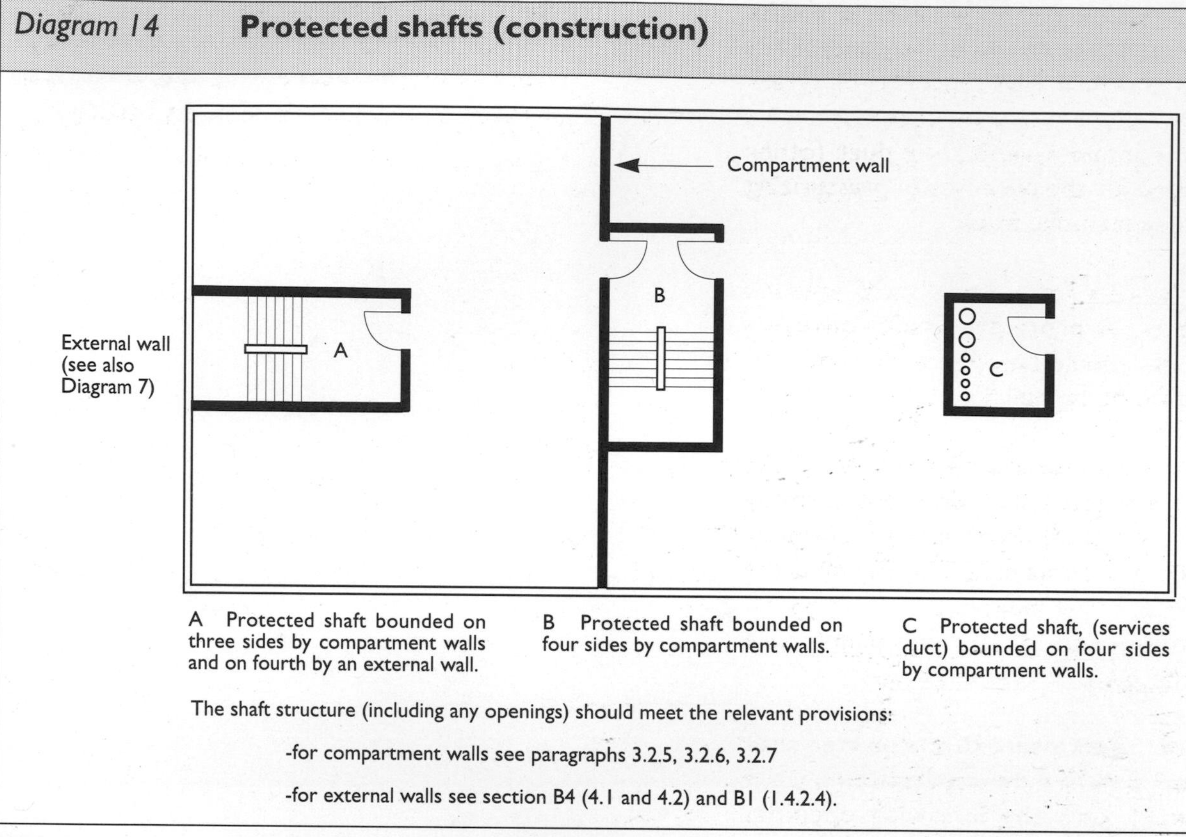

A Protected shaft bounded on three sides by compartment walls and on fourth by an external wall.

B Protected shaft bounded on four sides by compartment walls.

C Protected shaft, (services duct) bounded on four sides by compartment walls.

The shaft structure (including any openings) should meet the relevant provisions:

-for compartment walls see paragraphs 3.2.5, 3.2.6, 3.2.7

-for external walls see section B4 (4.1 and 4.2) and B1 (1.4.2.4).

Diagram 15 **Glazed screen separating protected shaft from lobby or corridor** *Par. 3.2.7.3 Table A1*

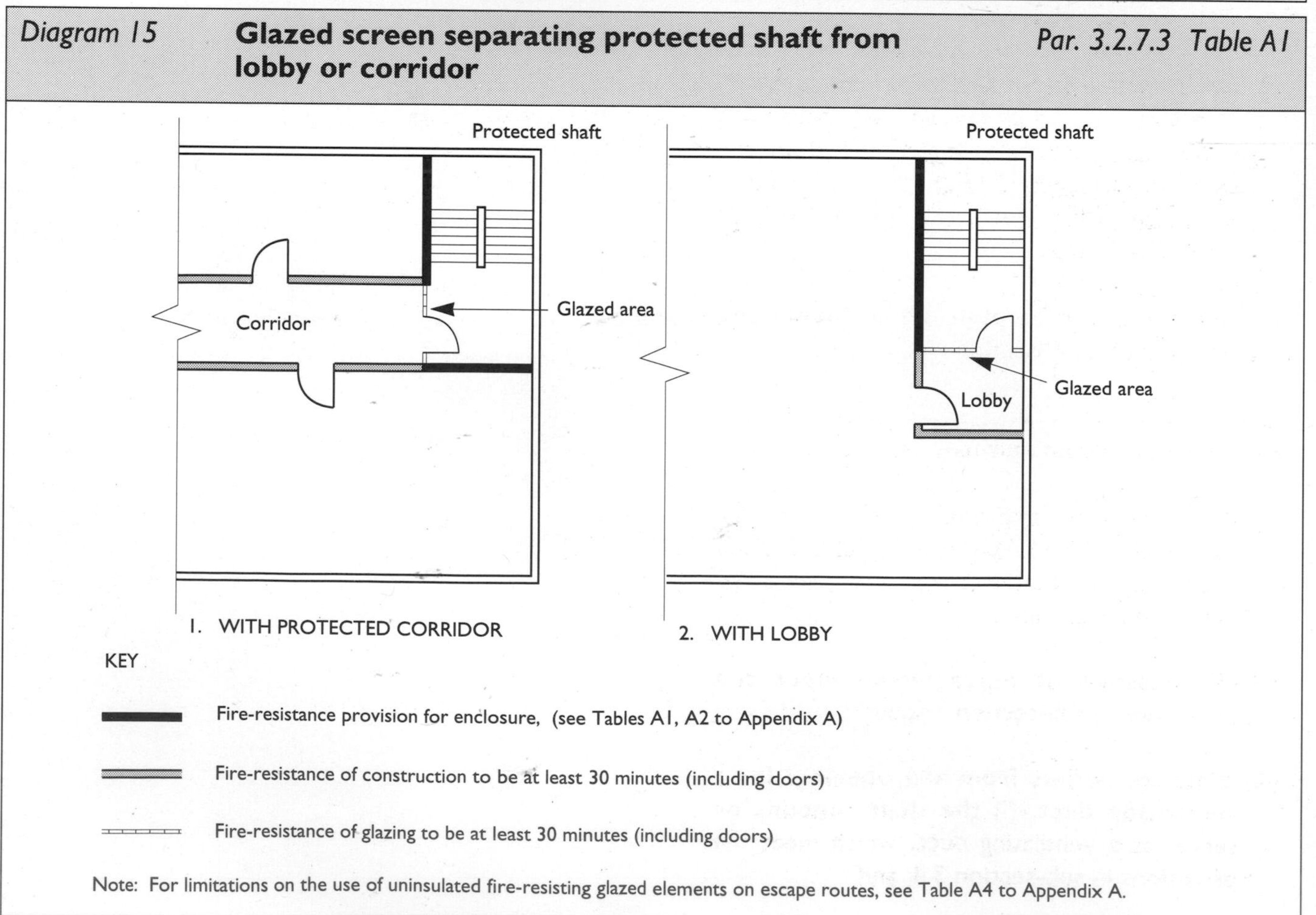

1. WITH PROTECTED CORRIDOR

2. WITH LOBBY

KEY

Fire-resistance provision for enclosure, (see Tables A1, A2 to Appendix A)

Fire-resistance of construction to be at least 30 minutes (including doors)

Fire-resistance of glazing to be at least 30 minutes (including doors)

Note: For limitations on the use of uninsulated fire-resisting glazed elements on escape routes, see Table A4 to Appendix A.

3.2.7.4 Pipes for oil or gas in protected shafts - If a protected shaft contains a stairway and/or lift, it should not also contain a pipe conveying oil or gas (other than hydraulic oil in the mechanism of a hydraulic lift) or contain a ventilating duct (other than a duct provided for the purposes of pressurizing the stairway to keep it smoke free).

3.2.7.5 Ventilation of protected shafts conveying gas - A protected shaft conveying piped flammable gas should be adequately ventilated direct to the outside of the building.

3.2.7.6 Openings into protected shafts - An external wall of a protected shaft does not normally need to have fire resistance, unless it is a fire-fighting shaft, (see B5), or if it contains a stairway, and the layout is such that it may expose persons to risk. Openings in other parts of the enclosure to a protected shaft should be limited as follows:

(a) Where part of the enclosure to a protected shaft is a wall common to two or more buildings (i.e. a separating wall), only the following openings should be made in that wall:

  (i) a door which is needed to provide a means of escape in case of fire and which has the same fire resistance as that required for the wall (see Appendix B, Table B1) and is fitted in accordance with the provisions of Appendix B; and

  (ii) the passage of a pipe which meets the provisions in sub-section 3.4.

(b) Other parts of the enclosure (other than an external wall) should only have openings for:

  (i) doors which have the appropriate fire resistance given in Appendix B, Table B1, and are fitted in accordance with the provisions of Appendix B; and

  (ii) the passage of pipes which meet the provisions in sub-section 3.4; and

  (iii) inlets to, outlets from and openings for a ventilation duct, (if the shaft contains or serves as a ventilating duct) which meet the provisions in sub-section 3.4; and

  (iv) the passage of lift cables into a lift motor room (if the shaft contains a lift). If the motor room is at the bottom of the shaft, the openings should be as small as practicable.

3.3 Concealed Spaces (Cavities)

Introduction

3.3.1 Hidden voids in the construction of a building provide a ready route for smoke and flame spread. This is particularly so in the case of voids above other spaces in a building, e.g. above a suspended ceiling or in a roof space. As the spread is concealed, it presents a greater danger than would a more obvious weakness in the fabric of the building. Provisions are made to restrict this by interrupting cavities which could form a pathway around a barrier to fire, and sub-dividing extensive cavities.

It should be noted that cavity barriers should not be provided above compartment walls as these walls are required to be carried up full storey height, to a compartment floor or to the roof as appropriate, (see 3.2.5.10). The fire resistance standards for cavity barriers are lower than for a compartment wall, and it is important to use a compartment wall in this situation to maintain the standard of fire resistance.

Provision of Cavity Barriers

3.3.2 Cavity barriers should be provided in accordance with Table 3.2 in specified locations for different purpose groups.

The dimensions of concealed spaces should be in accordance with the provisions outlined in 3.3.3.

Diagram 16 illustrates the need for cavity barriers at the intersection of fire resisting construction and elements containing a concealed space.

Diagram 16 **Interrupting concealed spaces (cavities)** *Par. 3.3.2*

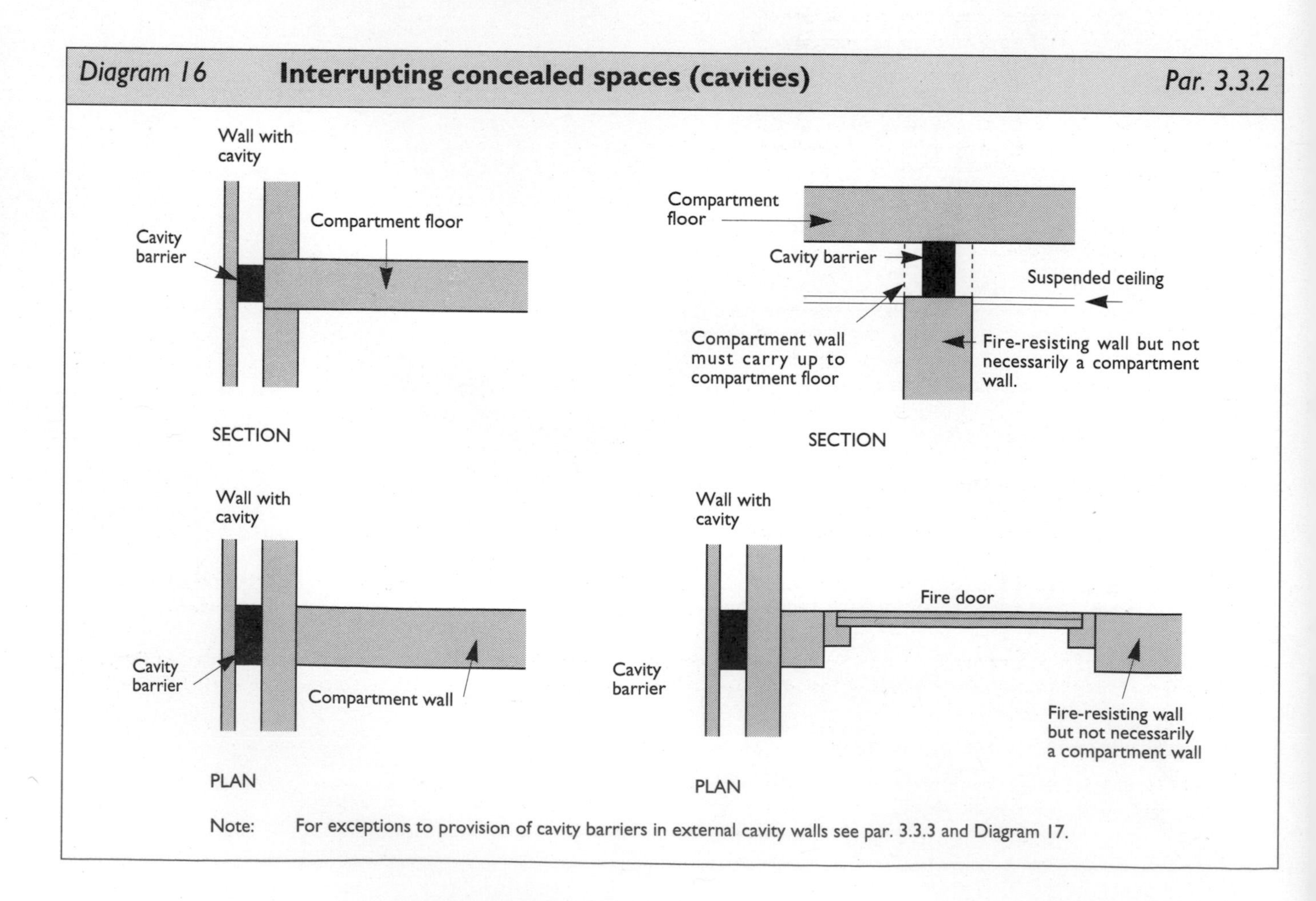

Note: For exceptions to provision of cavity barriers in external cavity walls see par. 3.3.3 and Diagram 17.

Table 3.2 **Provision of cavity barriers**

	Cavity Barriers to be provided	**Purpose Group in which the provision applies**			
		1(a) & 1(b)	**1(c)**	**2(a) & 2(b)**	**3-8**
1.	At the junction between an external cavity wall which does not comply with Diagram 17, and a separating wall.	ø	ø	ø	ø
2.	Above the enclosures to a protected stairway in a house of 3 or more storeys (see Diagram 18(a)(1).	ø	-	-	-
3.	At the junction between an external cavity wall which does not comply with Diagram 17, and every compartment floor and compartment wall.	-	ø	ø	ø
4.	At the junction between a cavity wall which does not comply with Diagram 17, and every compartment floor, compartment wall, or other wall or door assembly which forms a fire-resisting barrier.	-	ø	ø	ø
5.	In a protected escape route, above any fire-resisting construction which is not carried full storey height, or (in the case of a top storey) to the underside of the roof covering (1).	-	ø	ø	ø
6.	Above any bedroom partitions which are not carried full storey height, or (in the case of a top storey) to the underside of the roof covering (1).	-	-	ø	-
7.	Where a corridor (which is not a protected corridor) should be sub-divided to prevent fire or smoke from affecting the routes to two exits simultaneously (see B1, sub-section 1.2 and Diagram 20(a)), above any corridor enclosures which are not carried full storey height, or (in the case of a top storey) to the underside of the roof covering (2).	-	-	-	ø
8.	To sub-divide any cavity (including any roof space) so that the distance between cavity barriers does not exceed the dimensions given in Table 3.3.	-	-	-	ø

Notes:

ø denotes that provision of cavity barriers apply.

- denotes that provision of cavity barriers do not apply.

(1) The provisions in items 2, 5 and 6 of this table does not apply where the cavity is enclosed on the lower side by a fire-resisting ceiling (as shown in Diagram 19 and Diagram 18(b)) which extends throughout the building, compartment or separated part.

(2) The provision in item 7 of this table does not apply where the storey is sub-divided by fire-resisting construction carried full storey height and passing through the line of sub-division of the corridor (see Diagram 20(b)), or where the cavity is enclosed on the lower side as described in Note (1).

Diagram 17 **Cavity walls excluded from provisions for cavity barriers** *Table 3.2 Par. 3.3.3*

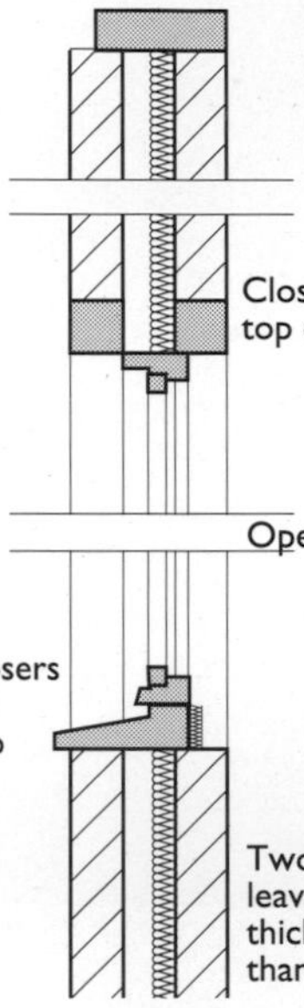

Close cavity at top of wall unless totally filled with insulation

Close cavity at top of opening

Opening

Cavity closers at cill and jambs also

Two block or brick leaves at least 75 mm thick. Cavity not more than 110 mm wide

Cavity wall

SECTION

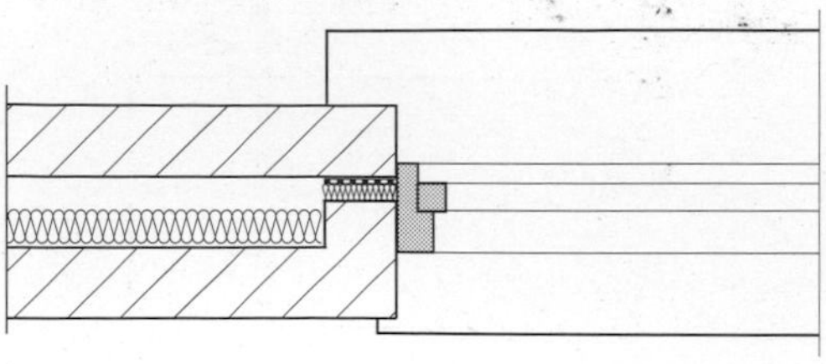

PLAN

Combustible material should not be placed in or exposed to the cavity except for:

(a) Timber lintel, window or door frame, or end of timber joist

(b) Pipe, conduit or cable

(c) DPC, flashing closer or wall tie

(d) Domestic meter cupboard provided that
- there are not more than two cupboards to a dwelling
- the opening in the outer wall leaf is not more than 800 mm x 500 mm for each cupboard, and
- the inner leaf is not penetrated except by a sleeve not more than 80 mm x 80 mm which is firestopped.

Diagram 18 **Roofspaces over protected stairway in dwelling houses of three or more storeys** (alternative arrangements) *Table 3.2*

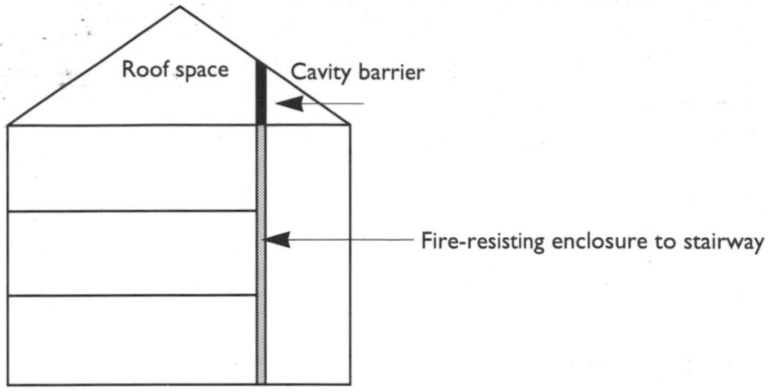

Roof space

Cavity barrier

Fire-resisting enclosure to stairway

(a) WITH CAVITY BARRIER(S)

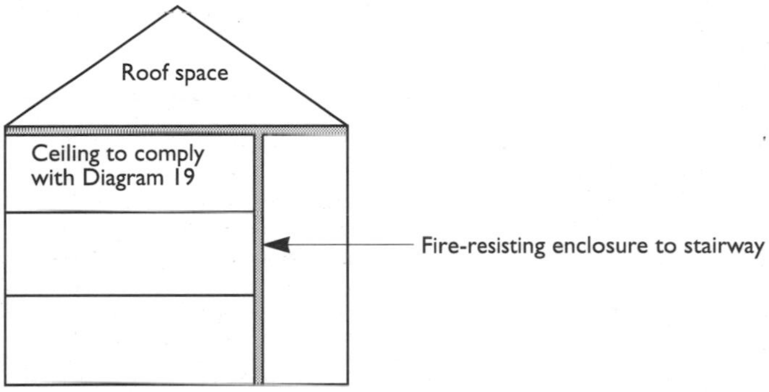

Roof space

Ceiling to comply with Diagram 19

Fire-resisting enclosure to stairway

(b) WITH FIRE-RESISTING CEILING

Diagram 19 **Fire resisting ceiling below a concealed space** *Table 3.2*

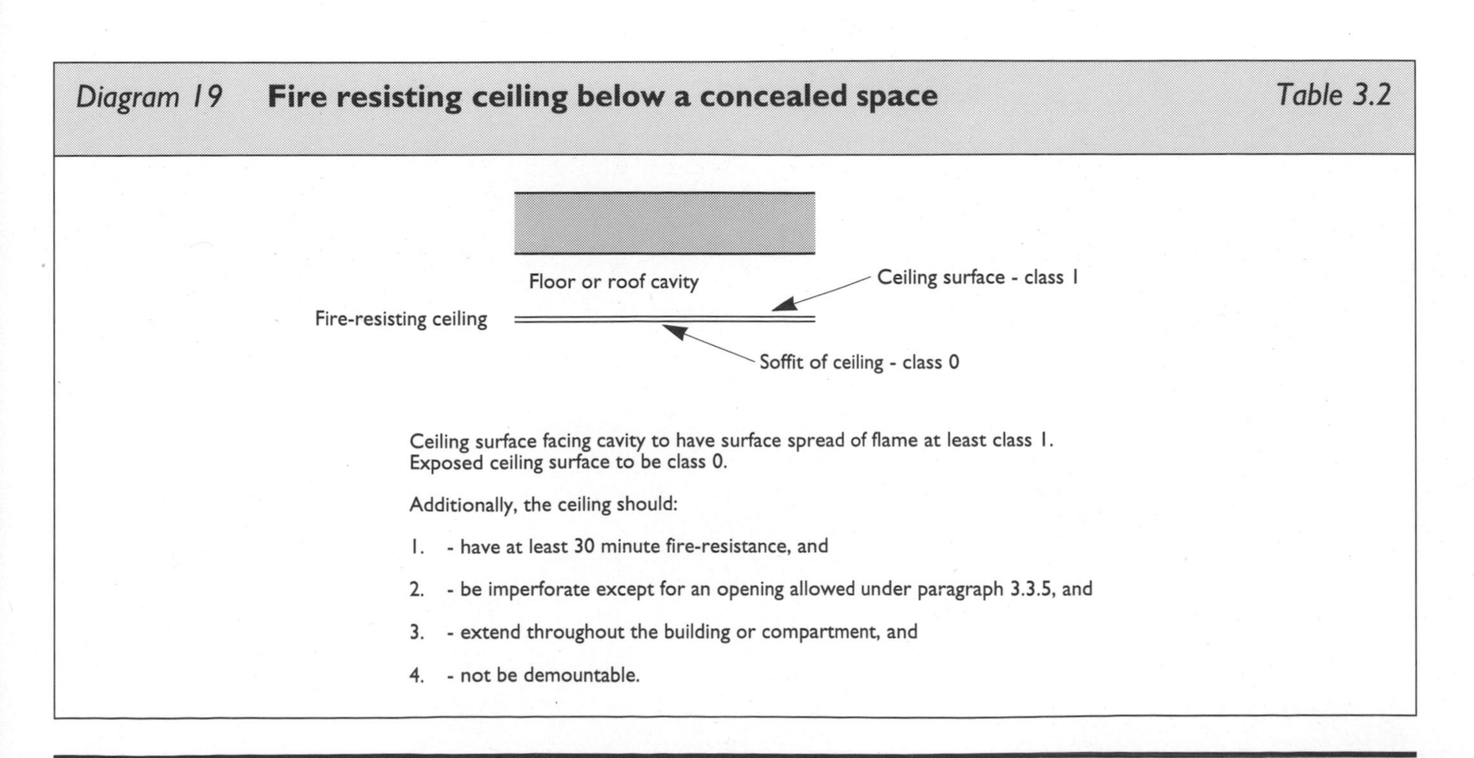

Ceiling surface facing cavity to have surface spread of flame at least class 1.
Exposed ceiling surface to be class 0.

Additionally, the ceiling should:

1. - have at least 30 minute fire-resistance, and

2. - be imperforate except for an opening allowed under paragraph 3.3.5, and

3. - extend throughout the building or compartment, and

4. - not be demountable.

Diagram 20 **Corridor subdivision** (alternative arrangements) *Table 3.2*

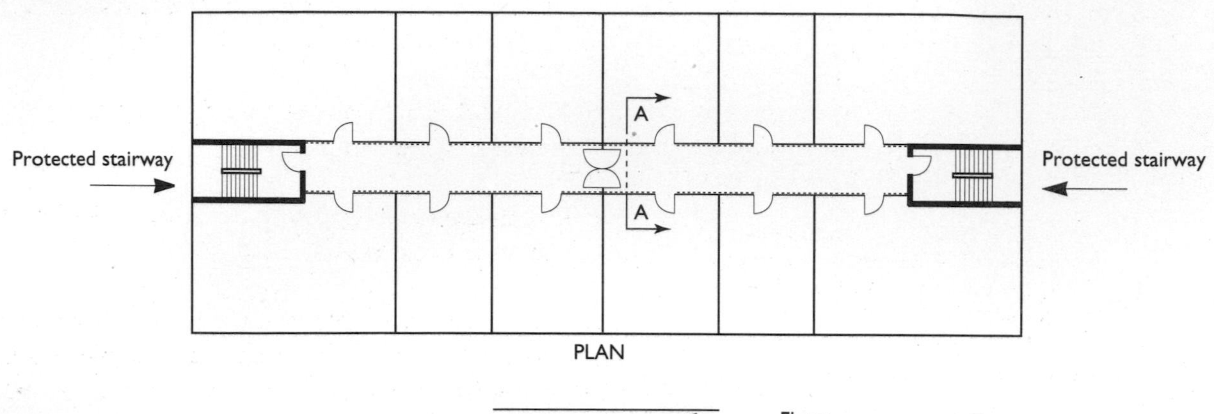

PLAN

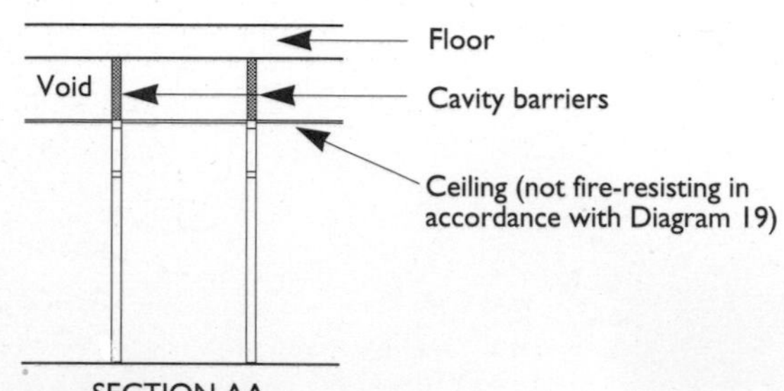

SECTION AA
Cavity barriers in ceiling void over corridor walls

(a) CAVITY BARRIERS ABOVE CORRIDOR ENCLOSURE

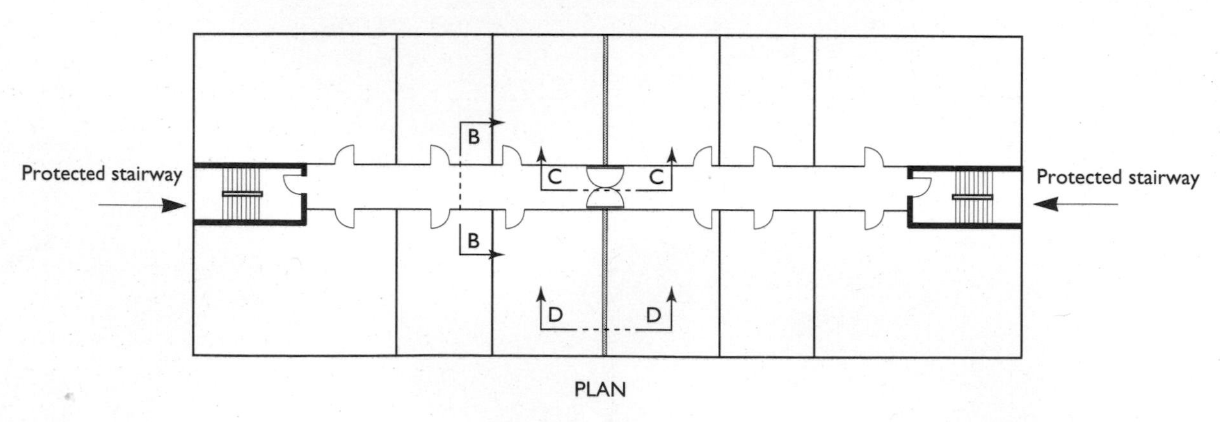

PLAN

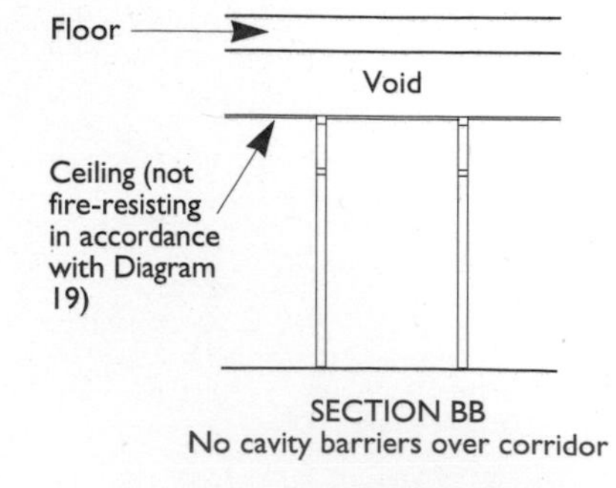

SECTION BB
No cavity barriers over corridor

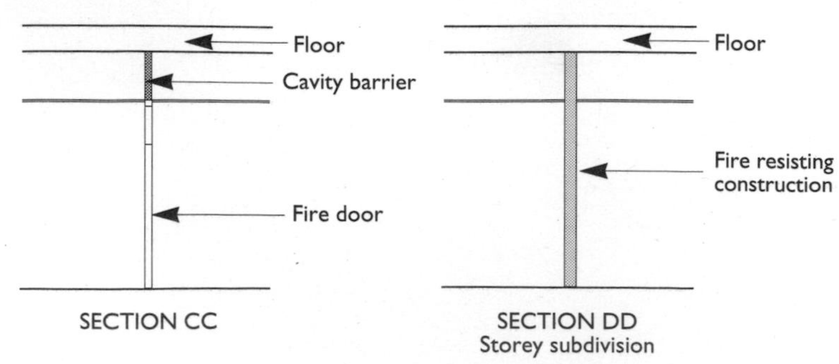

SECTION CC

SECTION DD
Storey subdivision

(b) SUBDIVISION OF STOREY

Maximum Dimensions of Concealed Spaces

3.3.3 The dimensions of cavities (i.e. the maximum un-divided concealed space) should not exceed those specified in Table 3.3.

Table 3.3 **Maximum dimensions of cavities**

Location of Cavity	Class of surface exposed In cavity (excluding surface of any pipe, cable or conduit, or insulation to any pipe)	Maximum dimension in any direction (m)
Between a roof and a ceiling	Any	20
Any other cavity	Class I	20
	Any other class	10

The provisions of Table 3.3 do not apply to any cavity described at (1) to (8) below:

(1) Where any room under a cavity exceeds the dimensions given, cavity barriers need only be provided on the line of the enclosing walls/partitions of that room - subject to cavity barriers not being more than 40 m apart in any direction;

(2) Where the cavity is over an undivided area and is used as a plenum and exceeds 40 m (in both directions on plan), there is no limit to the size of the cavity if:

(a) the room and the cavity together are compartmented from the rest of the building;

(b) an automatic fire detection and alarm system is fitted in the building with smoke detectors in the cavity and in the return air ducting, and which stops circulation of the ventilation system and switches it to extract;

(c) the suspended ceiling and its supports are of non-combustible construction;

(d) the flame spread rating of any pipe insulation system is Class 1;

(e) any electrical wiring in the void is laid in metal trays or in metal conduit; and

(f) any other materials in the cavity are of limited combustibility.

(3) in a wall which should be fire-resisting only because it is loadbearing;

(4) in a masonry or concrete external cavity wall as shown in Diagram 17;

(5) in a floor or a roof space where the cavity is enclosed on the lower side by a fire-resisting ceiling (as shown in Diagram 19) which extends throughout the building, compartment or separated part, subject to a limit of 30 m on the extent of any such cavity;

(6) below a floor next to the ground or oversite concrete, if the cavity is less than 1m in height or if the cavity is not normally accessible by persons, unless there are openings in the floor such that it is possible for litter to accumulate in the cavity (in which case cavity barriers should be provided, and access should be provided to the cavity for cleaning);

(7) formed by over-cladding an existing masonry (or concrete) external wall, or an existing concrete roof, provided that the cavity does not contain combustible insulation; and

(8) between double-skinned corrugated or profiled insulated roof and wall sheeting if the sheeting is a material of limited combustibility and both surfaces of the insulating layer have a surface spread of flame of at least Class 1 (see Appendix A) and make contact with the inner and outer skins of cladding (see Diagram 21).

Diagram 21 **Double-skinned insulated roof and wall sheeting excluded from provisions in Table 3.3** *Par. 3.3.3*

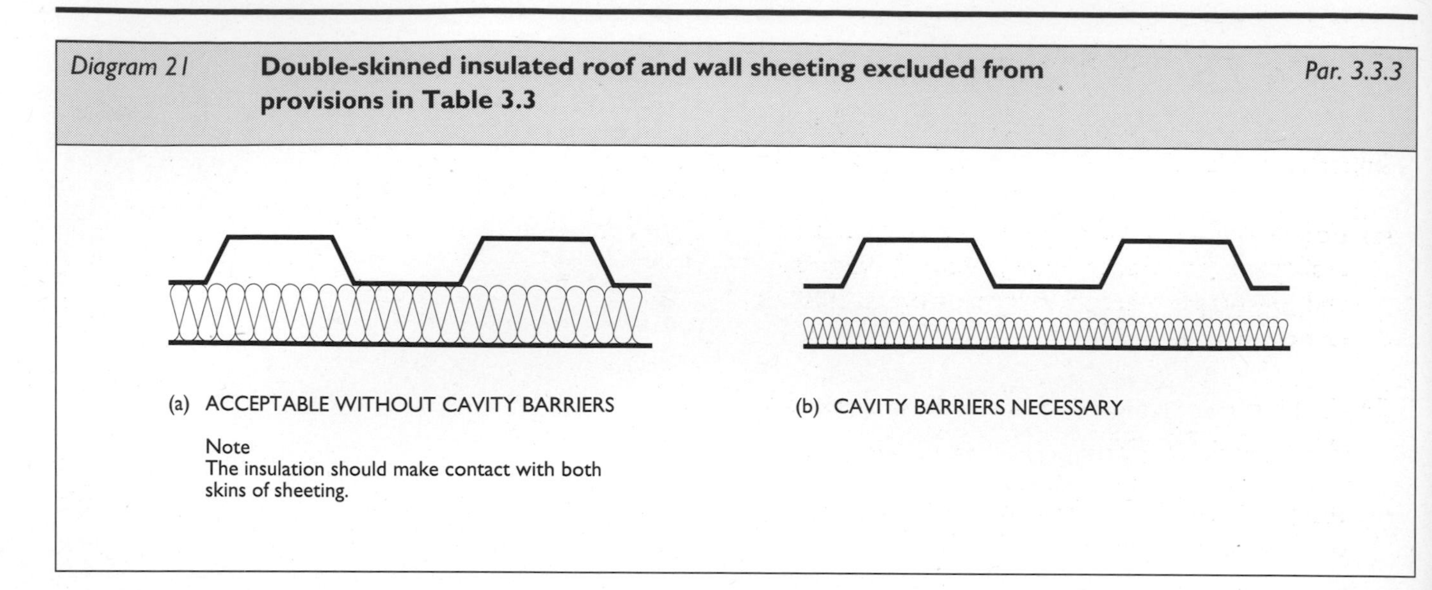

Construction and Fixings for Cavity Barriers

3.3.4 Every cavity barrier should be constructed to provide at least 30 minutes fire resistance (see Appendix A, Table A1, item 16).

Notes:

(a) any cavity barrier required in a stud wall or partition may, however, be formed of -

(i) steel at least 0.5 mm thick, or

(ii) timber at least 38 mm thick, or

(iii) polythene sleeved mineral wool, or mineral wool slab, in either case under compression when installed in the cavity.

(b) a cavity barrier may be formed by any construction provided for another purpose if it meets the provisions for cavity barriers.

Cavity barriers should be tightly fitted to rigid construction and mechanically fixed in position wherever possible. Where this is not possible (for example, in the case of a junction with slates, tiles, corrugated sheeting or similar materials) the junction should be fire-stopped.

Cavity barriers should also be fixed so that their performance is unlikely to be made ineffective by:

(a) movement of the building due to subsidence, shrinkage or thermal change;

(b) collapse in a fire of any services penetrating them;

(c) failure in a fire of their fixings; or

(d) failure in a fire of any material or construction which they abut.

For example, if a suspended ceiling is continued over the top of a fire-resisting wall or partition and direct connection is made between the ceiling and the cavity barrier above the line of the wall or partition, premature failure of the cavity barrier can occur when the ceiling collapses. However, this does not arise if the ceiling is designed to provide fire protection of 30 minutes or more.

Openings in Cavity Barriers

3.3.5 Any openings in a cavity barrier should be limited to those for:

(a) doors which have at least 20 minutes fire resistance (see Appendix B, Table B1, item 8(a)) and are fitted in accordance with the provisions of Appendix B; and

(b) the passage of pipes which meet the provisions in sub-section 3.4; and

(c) the passage of cables or conduits containing one or more cables; and

(d) openings fitted with a suitably mounted automatic fire shutter; and

(e) ducts which (unless they are fire-resisting) are fitted with a suitably mounted automatic fire shutter where they pass through the cavity barrier.

3.4. Protection of Openings and Fire-Stopping

Introduction

3.4.1 Earlier sections of this Document describe the provision of barriers to fire, and the circumstances in which there may be openings in them. This Section deals with the protection of openings in such barriers.

If an element that is intended to provide fire separation (i.e. it has requirements for fire resistance in terms of integrity and insulation) is to be effective, then every joint, or imperfection of fit, or opening to allow services to pass through the element, should be adequately protected by sealing or fire-stopping so that the fire resistance of the element is not impaired. Building service installations should be designed in accordance with BS 8313: 1989 (section 12). The provisions of this Section also apply to openings in protected corridors which are provided for the protection of the means of escape (see B1).

Provisions for door openings and fire doors are given in Appendix B because they are relevant to B1 and B5, as well as B3.

The measures are intended to delay the passage of fire. They generally have the additional benefit of retarding smoke spread but the test specified in Appendix A for integrity does not stipulate criteria for the passage of smoke as such.

Openings for Pipes

3.4.2 Pipes which pass through a compartment wall or compartment floor (unless the pipe is in a protected shaft), or cavity barrier, should meet the appropriate provisions in alternatives A, B or C below.

Alternative A: Proprietary Seals (any pipe diameter)

Provide a proprietary sealing system which has been shown by test to maintain the fire resistance of the wall, floor or cavity barrier.

Alternative B: Pipes with a restricted diameter

Where a proprietary sealing system is not used, fire-stopping may be used around the pipe, keeping the opening as small as possible. The nominal internal diameter of the pipe should not be more than the relevant dimension given in Table 3.4.

The diameters given in Table 3.4 for pipes of specification (b) used in situation (2) assume that the pipes are part of an above ground drainage system and are enclosed as shown in Diagram 22. If they are not, the smaller diameter given in situation (3) should be used instead.

Alternative C: Sleeving

A pipe of lead, aluminium, aluminium alloy, asbestos-cement or uPVC, with a maximum nominal internal diameter of 160 mm, may be used with a sleeving of non-combustible pipe as shown in Diagram 23. The specification for non-combustible and uPVC pipes is given in the notes to Table 3.4.

Ventilating Ducts

3.4.3 Ventilation and air conditioning ducts which pass from one compartment to another should be protected in accordance with the recommendations contained in BS 5588: Part 9 Code of practice for ventilation and air conditioning ductwork.

Flues, etc.

3.4.4 If a flue, or duct containing flues or appliance ventilation duct(s), passes through a compartment wall or compartment floor, or is built into a compartment wall, the walls of the flue or duct should have a fire resistance of at least half that of the wall or floor in order to prevent the by-passing of the compartmentation (see Diagram 24). The walls enclosing the flue or duct should be of solid non-combustible construction.

Fire-Stopping

3.4.5 In addition to any other provisions in this document for fire-stopping:

(a) joints between elements which serve as a barrier to the passage of fire should be fire-stopped; and

(b) all openings for pipes, ducts, conduits or cables to pass through any part of an element which serves as a barrier to the passage of fire should be -

(i) kept as few in number as possible, and

(ii) kept as small as practicable, and

(iii) fire-stopped (which in the case of a pipe or ducts, should allow thermal movement).

To prevent displacement, materials used for fire-stopping should be reinforced with (or supported by) materials of limited combustibility in the following circumstances:

(a) in all cases where the unsupported span is greater than 100 mm, and

(b) in any other case where non-rigid materials are used (unless they have been shown to be satisfactory by test).

Proprietary sealing systems (including those designed for service penetrations) which have been shown by test to maintain the fire resistance of the wall or other element are available.

Other suitable fire-stopping materials include:

- cement or lime mortar,
- gypsum based plaster,
- cement or gypsum based vermiculite/perlite mixes,
- glass, crushed rock, blast furnace slag or ceramic based products (with or without resin binders), and
- intumescent mastics.

These may be used only in situations which are suitable for the particular fire-stopping materials.

Table 3.4 **Maximum nominal internal diameter of pipes**

Purpose	**(a)**	**(b)**	**(c)**
	Non-combustible material (1)	**Lead, aluminium or aluminium alloy, fibre- cement or uPVC (2)**	**any other material**
1. Structure (but not separating wall) enclosing a protected shaft which is not a stairway or lift shaft	160	110	40
2. Separating wall between dwelling houses (4), or compartment wall or compartment floor between flats	160	160 (stack pipe)(3) 110 (branch pipe)(3)	40
3. Any other situation	160	40	40

Notes:

1. A non-combustible material (such as cast iron or steel) which, if exposed to a temperature of 800°C will neither soften nor fracture to the extent that flame or hot gases will pass through the wall of the pipe.

2. uPVC pipes complying with BS 4514: 1983, and uPVC pipes complying with BS 5255: 1989.

3. Pipes forming part of an above ground drainage system and enclosed as shown in Diagram 22.

4. See 3.2.5.5 for situations where no pipes, wires or other services are allowed in separating walls between houses.

Diagram 22 Enclosures for drainage or water supply pipes *Par. 3.4.2*

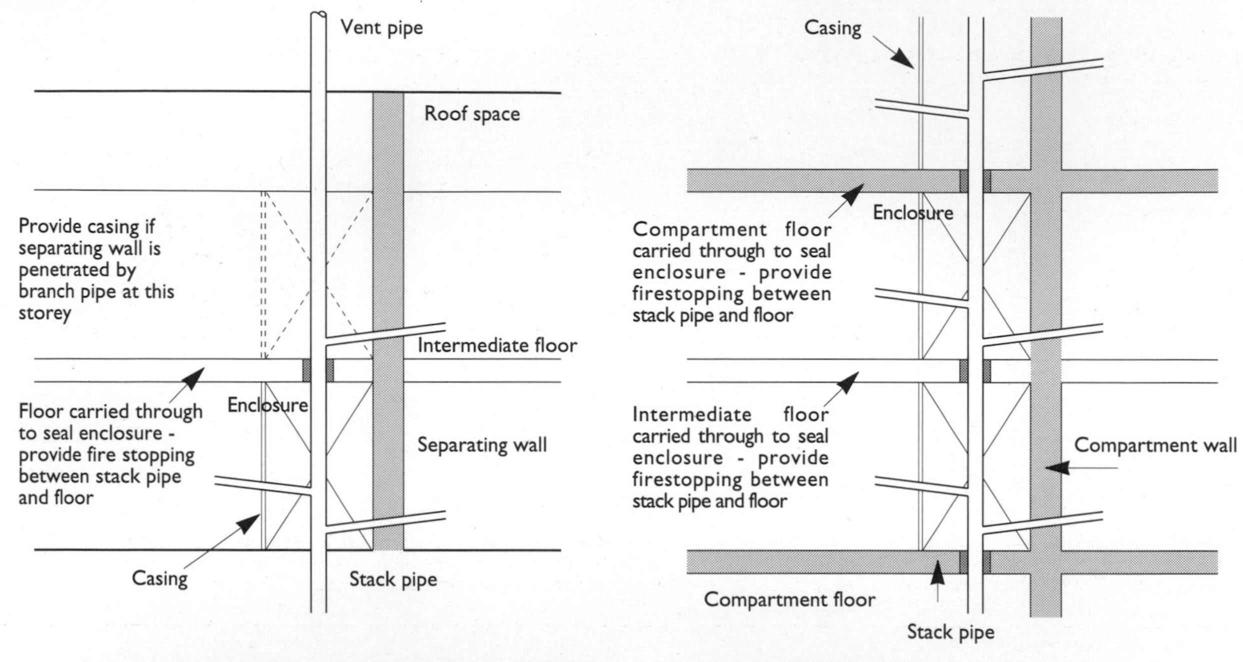

(a) DWELLING HOUSE WITH ANY NUMBER OF STOREYS

(b) OTHER BUILDINGS

Notes

1. The enclosure should:
   (a) be bounded by a separating wall, a compartment wall or floor, an outside wall, an intermediate floor, or a casing (see specification at 2 below), and
   (b) have internal surfaces (except framing members) of Class O, and
   (c) not have an access panel which opens into a circulation space or a bedroom, and
   (d) be used only for drainage, water supply or vent pipes.

2. The casing should:

   (a) be imperforate except for an opening for a pipe or an access panel, and
   (b) not be of sheet metal, and
   (c) have not less than 30 minute fire resistance, including any access panel.

3. The opening for a pipe, either in the structure or the casing, should be as small as possible and firestopped around the pipe.

Diagram 23 Pipes penetrating a compartment wall or floor (sleeving) *Par. 3.4.2*

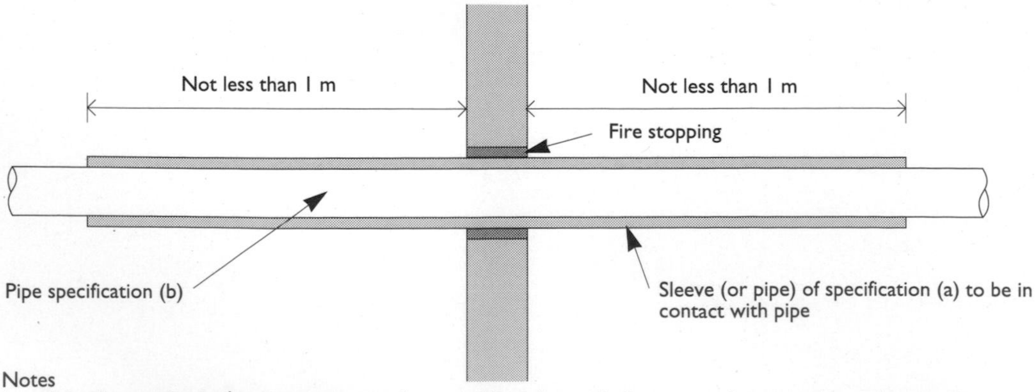

Not less than 1 m

Not less than 1 m

Fire stopping

Pipe specification (b)

Sleeve (or pipe) of specification (a) to be in contact with pipe

Notes

1. Make the opening in the structure as small as possible and provide firestopping between pipe and structure.
2. See Table 3.4 for materials specification.

Diagram 24 **Flues and compartment walls or floors** *Par. 3.4.4*

1. FLUE PASSING THROUGH COMPARTMENT WALL OR FLOOR

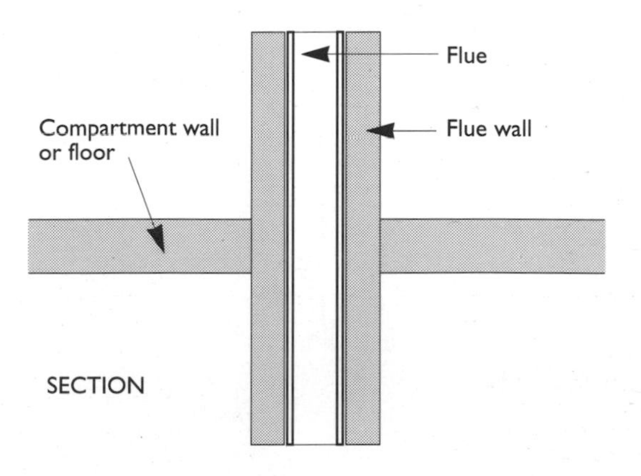

Flue walls should have a fire resistance of at least one half of that required for the compartment wall or floor, and be of non-combustible construction.

2. FLUE BUILT INTO COMPARTMENT WALL

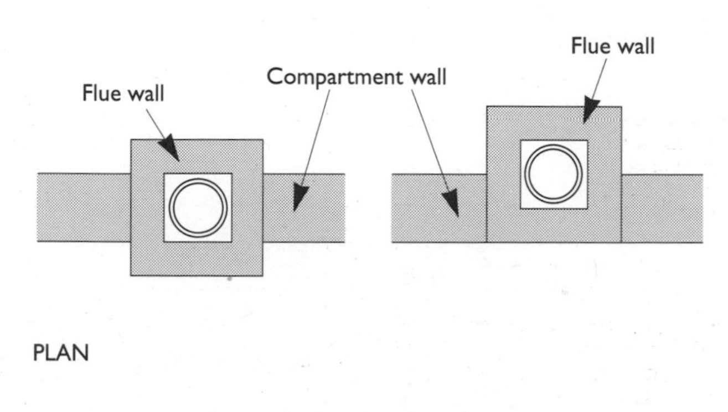

In each case flue walls should have a fire resistance of at least one half of that required for the compartment wall and be of non-combustible construction.

3.5 Special Provisions

Introduction

3.5.1 This Section describes additional considerations which apply to the design and construction of Car Parks, Shopping Centres, Residential (Institutional) buildings and buildings containing an atrium.

Car Parks

3.5.2 Buildings or parts of buildings used as parking for cars and other light vehicles are unlike other buildings in certain respects, and merit some departures from the usual provisions for the restriction of fire spread within buildings because:

- the fire load is well defined; and
- there is evidence that fire spread is not likely to occur between one vehicle and another, in well-ventilated above ground parking, and there is a correspondingly low probability of fire spread from one storey to another. Ventilation is all important in car parks, and as heat and smoke cannot be dissipated so readily from a car park that is not open-sided fewer concessions are made.

3.5.2.1 Provisions common to all car park buildings - All materials used in the construction of the building, compartment or separated part should be non-combustible, except for:

(a) any surface finish applied -

(i) to a floor or roof of the car park, or

(ii) within any adjoining building, compartment or separated part to the structure enclosing the car park,

if the finish meets any relevant provisions in B2 and B4;

(b) any fire door; and

(c) any attendants kiosk not exceeding 15 m² in area.

3.5.2.2 Open-sided car parks - If the building, or separated part containing the car park, complies with the following provisions (in addition to those in par. 3.5.2.1) it may be regarded as an open sided car park for the purposes of fire resistance assessment in Appendix A, Table A2, and for the purposes of space separation in B4, Table 4.3, it may be regarded as a small building or compartment.

(a) There should not be any basement storeys.

(b) Each storey should be naturally ventilated by permanent openings at each level having an aggregate area not less than 5% of the floor area at that level, of which at least half should be in two opposing walls.

(c) If the building is also used for any other purpose, the part forming the car park is a separated part (see Appendix D for definition).

3.5.2.3 Car parks which are not open sided - Where it is not possible to provide the degree of natural ventilation set out in par. 3.5.2.2 above, the building is not classified as open sided and a different standard of fire resistance is required (refer to Table A2, Appendix A). Such car parks require ventilation, which may be by natural or mechanical means. Provisions are set out in pars. 3.5.2.4 and 3.5.2.5 below. The provisions in par. 3.5.2.1 above apply in all cases.

3.5.2.4 Natural ventilation - Where car parks are not open sided, each storey should be naturally ventilated by permanent openings at each level having an aggregate area not less than 2.5% of the floor area at that level, of which at least half should be in two opposing walls. The number and disposition of smoke outlets should be such as to maximise the effectiveness of the ventilation.

Smoke vents at ceiling level may be used as an alternative to the provision of permanent openings in the walls. They should have an aggregate area of permanent opening totalling not less than 2.5% of the floor area and be arranged to provide a through draught.

3.5.2.5 Mechanical ventilation - In some basement car parks, and enclosed car parks, it may not be possible to obtain the minimum standard of natural ventilation openings set out in par. 3.5.2.4 above. In such cases a system of mechanical ventilation should be provided as follows:

(a) the system should be independent of any other ventilating system and be designed to operate at 6 air changes per hour for normal petrol vapour extraction, and at 10 air changes per hour in a fire condition;

(b) the system should be designed to run in two parts, each part capable of extracting 50% of the rates set out in (a) above, and designed so that each part may operate singly or simultaneously;

(c) each part of the system should have an independent power supply which would operate in the event of failure of the main supply;

(d) outlets for exhaust air should be arranged so that 50% of the outlets are at high level, and 50% at low level; and

(e) the fans should be rated to run at 300°C for a minimum of 60 mins, and the ductwork and fixings should be constructed of materials having a melting point not less than 800°C.

Shopping Centres (Purpose Group 4(b))

3.5.3 Whilst the provisions in this Document about shops should generally be capable of application in cases where a shop is contained in a single separate building, complications may arise where a shop forms part of a shopping centre. A shopping centre may include covered malls providing access to a number of shops and common servicing areas. In particular, the provisions about fire resistance, separating walls, surfaces and boundary distances may pose problems.

To ensure a satisfactory standard of fire safety in shopping complexes, alternative measures and additional compensatory features to those set out in this document would be appropriate (see 0.2). While this section is concerned with matters related to internal fire spread by way of the structure, these measures will involve consideration of all aspects of fire safety and their inter-action is particularly critical in these buildings.

The measures that are relevant to B3 include:

(a) sprinkler protection of all shop units, storage and service areas, and any parts of malls used for a purpose that might introduce a fire load into the mall;

(b) construction consisting generally of materials of limited combustibility except for limited decorative features and limited amounts of materials in shop fascias having a lesser standard of surface spread of flame characteristics than those for walls in circulation areas (see also B2);

(c) compartmentation requirements (see 3.2.4.7) including the following:

- walls and floors between shop units constructed as compartment walls and compartment floors;

- floors in any shop unit exceeding 2000 m^2 plan area of largest floor constructed as compartment floors;

- floors in any shop unit opening onto a mall at more than one level constructed as compartment floors; and

- compartmentation also provided between a large shop unit (over 3700 m^2) and a mall, or between opposing large shop units (each over 2000 m^2) and a mall. This compartmentation could be provided by fire shutters (smaller shop units would normally not be compartmented from a mall);

(d) fire resistance periods for loadbearing elements of structure which are appropriate to the nature of the occupancies and the overall size of the building.

The above items are not exhaustive but draw attention to the need to consider proposals for shopping complexes as a comprehensive fire safety package. Guidance on these matters is set out in BS 5588: Part 10: 1991 Code of practice for shopping complexes.

Guidance on smoke control measures in enclosed shopping centres is contained in the Building Research Establishment Report (BR 186) Design principles for smoke ventilation in enclosed shopping centres.

Residential (Institutional) Buildings (Purpose Group 2(a))

3.5.4 In the case of Residential (Institutional) buildings, consideration is required to the potential for fire spread between compartments by way of the external elevations. This is on account of the nature of the occupancy and the need to ensure the safety of occupants who have been evacuated to an adjoining compartment (see 1.2.7).

The potential for fire spread by way of unprotected areas on each side of a compartment wall or protected stairway should be considered, where such walls abut an external elevation or are in close proximity to a re-entrant angle, such as occurs in the corner of a courtyard or the internal angle where two elevations meet.

In the case of courtyards, lightwells or wings of the same building, where opposite elevations are wholly or partially in different compartments, separation distances between such opposing elevations should be considered.

Guidance on internal fire spread (structure) in hospitals, including the considerations referred to above, is contained in Firecode Health Technical Memorandum 81, Fire Precautions in New Hospitals, 1996 (HTM81:1996).

Hospitals also contain a number of high hazard rooms and areas which should be regarded as places of special fire risk (see 1.0.9). These include physiotherapy rooms, occupational therapy rooms, laundries, large kitchens and laboratories. Such areas should be fully separated by means of compartmentation (see 3.2.4.1).

Buildings Containing an Atrium

3.5.5 Many large modern buildings contain an atrium, which is a large undivided space within a building (see 1.0.9 for definition). Storeys in the building may be open to the atrium or they may be separated by fire-resisting construction. The provision of an atrium will therefore impact on compartmentation and the possibility of fire spread between storeys. The accumulation of smoke which enters the atrium will also impact on the means of escape provisions (see Section B1).

Like a shopping centre, the design of a building containing an atrium may require alternative approaches to fire safety and the use of fire safety engineering (see 0.2). The measures that may be required will depend on the particular circumstances and will include consideration of all aspects of fire safety. The measures to be provided are likely to include:

- sprinkler protection to the building;

- smoke control measures within the atrium; and

- facilities to assist fire-fighting within the building;

Guidance on smoke control measures in buildings containing an atrium is contained in the Building Research Establishment Report (BR 258) Design approaches for smoke control in atrium buildings.

Section B4
External Fire Spread

External fire spread.	B4	The external walls and roof of a building shall be so designed and constructed that they afford adequate resistance to the spread of fire to and from neighbouring buildings.

Performance

The requirements of B4 may be met:

(a) if the external walls are constructed so that the risk of ignition from an external source, and the spread of fire over their surfaces, is restricted by making provision for them to have low rates of spread of flame, and in some cases low rates of heat release,

(b) if the amount of unprotected area in the side of the building is restricted so as to limit the amount of thermal radiation that can pass through the wall, taking the distance between the wall and the boundary into account, and

(c) if the roof is constructed so that the risk of spread of flame and/or fire penetration from an external fire source is restricted,

in each case so as to limit the risk of a fire spreading from the building to a building beyond the boundary, or vice versa.

The extent to which this is necessary is dependent on the use of the building, its distance from the boundary and (in some cases) its height.

Contents

4.0 Introduction to Provisions

4.0.1 The construction of external walls and the separation between buildings to prevent external fire spread are closely related.

The chances of fire spreading across an open space between buildings, and the consequences if it does, depend on:

- the size and intensity of the fire in the building concerned
- the risk it presents to people in the other building(s)
- the distance between the buildings, and
- the fire protection given by their facing sides

Provisions are made in sub-section 4.1 for the fire resistance of external walls, and to limit the susceptibility of the external surface of walls to ignition and to fire spread.

Provisions are made in sub-section 4.2 to limit the extent of openings and other unprotected areas in external walls in order to reduce the risk of fire spread by radiation.

Provisions are made in sub-section 4.3 for reducing the risk of fire spread between and over roofs.

Definitions

4.0.2 The following definitions apply specifically to B4. Other terms applicable more widely throughout this Document are given in Appendix D.

Boundary - The boundary of the land belonging to the building, or where the land abuts a road, railway, canal or river, the centreline of that road, railway, canal or river (see Diagram 25).

Class 0 - See Appendix A, par. A.10.

Conservatory - A single storey part of a building where the roof and walls are substantially glazed with a transparent or translucent material.

External wall - (or side of a building) includes a part of a roof pitched at an angle of 70° or more to the horizontal - if that part of the roof adjoins a space within the building to which persons have access (but not access only for repair or maintenance).

Notional boundary - A boundary presumed to exist between buildings on the same site (see Diagram 26).

Relevant boundary - The boundary which the side of the building faces (see Diagram 25). A notional boundary can be a relevant boundary.

Rooflight - Any domelight, lantern light, skylight or other element intended to admit daylight through a roof.

Thermo-plastic material - See Appendix A, paragraph A14.

Unprotected area - In relation to a side or external wall of a building means:

(a) a window, door or other opening, and

(b) any part of the external wall which has less than the relevant fire resistance set out in Section 4.1, and

(c) any part of the external wall which has combustible material more than 1 mm thick attached or applied to its external face, whether for cladding or any other purpose (combustible material in this context is any material that is not included in Tables A7 or A8 in Appendix A).

Provisions meeting the Requirement

4.1 Construction of External Walls

Introduction

4.1.1 Under B3, provisions are made in sub-section 3.1 for internal and external loadbearing walls to maintain their loadbearing function in the event of fire.

Provisions are made in this Section for the external walls of the building to have sufficient fire resistance to prevent fire spread across the relevant boundary. The provisions are closely linked with those for space separation in sub-section 4.2 which sets out limits on the amount of wall area that need not be fire-resisting (termed unprotected area). As the limits depend on the distance of the wall from the relevant boundary, it is possible for some, or all, of the walls to be permitted to have no fire resistance except for any parts which are loadbearing.

External walls are elements of structure and the relevant period of fire resistance (which is specified in Appendix A) depends on the use, height and size of the building concerned, and whether the wall is within 1 m of the relevant boundary.

Provisions are also made to restrict the amount of combustible surfaces on buildings that are very close (less than 1 m) to the relevant boundary and/or on high buildings. This is in order to reduce the susceptibility of ignition of the surface from an external source, and to reduce the possibility of fire spread up the external face of the building.

Fire Resistance Standard

4.1.2 The external walls of the building should have the appropriate fire resistance given in Appendix A, Table A1, unless they are permitted to form an unprotected area under sub-section 4.2.

Portal Frames

4.1.3 Portal frames are often used in single storey industrial and commercial buildings where there may be no provisions under B3 for fire resistance of the structure. Where, however, the building is near a relevant boundary, then the provisions in par. 4.1.2 require the external wall to be fire-resisting.

It is generally accepted that a portal frame acts as a single element because of the moment-resisting connections used, especially the column/rafter joints. Thus the rafter members of the frame, as well as the column members may need to be fire protected in cases where the external wall of the building cannot be wholly unprotected.

Following an investigation of the behaviour of steel portal frames in fire, it was considered technically and economically feasible to design the connection of the portal frame to the foundation so that it would transmit the overturning moment caused by the collapse in a fire of unprotected rafters, purlins and some roof cladding so as to allow the external wall to continue to perform its structural function. The design method is set out in "Fire and steel construction : the behaviour of steel portal frames in boundary conditions", published by the Steel Construction Institute, Silwood Park, Ascot, Berks, SL5 7QN, England.

Normally, portal frames of reinforced concrete can support external walls requiring the same degree of fire resistance without specific provision at the base to resist overturning.

External Surfaces

4.1.4 The external surfaces of walls should meet the provisions in Table 4.1. However, the total amount of combustible material may be limited in practice by the provisions for space separation in sub-section 4.2 (see par. 4.2.6).

Table 4.1	**Provision for external surface of walls**	
Maximum height of building (m)	**Distance from any point on the relevant boundary** *	
	Less than 1 m	1 m or more
20	Class 0	No provision (unless it is a building described in Note (1))
30	Class 0	Class 0 (2)
Over 30	Non-combustible (3)	Non-combustible (2)(4)

Notes:

* The relevant boundary might be a notional boundary.

(1) Any part of the wall of a building comprising flats or maisonettes, or a building in the Residential (Institutional), Other Residential, Assembly and recreation purpose groups, which is 10 m or less above the ground or above a roof or any other part of the building to which people have access, should have an index of performance (I) not more than 20 (timber cladding at least 9mm thick is also acceptable).

(2) Surfaces not more than 20 m above the ground may comprise any material with an index of performance (I) not more than 20. Timber cladding at least 9 mm thick is also acceptable.

(3) Surfaces not more than 30 m above the ground may be Class 0.

(4) Surfaces between 20 m and 30 m above the ground may be Class 0.

Index of performance (I) relates to performance under BS 476: Part 6, (see A9 of Appendix A).
For description of Class 0, see A10 of Appendix A.

4.2. Space Separation

Introduction

4.2.1 The provisions in this Section limit the extent of openings and other unprotected areas in the sides of the building (including areas with a combustible surface) which will not give adequate protection against the spread of fire.

The provisions assume:

(a) that the size of the fire will depend on the compartmentation of the building, so that the fire will involve a complete compartment, but will not spread across lines of compartmentation;

(b) that the intensity of the fire is related to the use of the building (i.e. purpose group), but that it can be moderated by a sprinkler system;

(c) that residential and assembly and recreation purpose groups represent a greater life risk than other uses;

(d) that the building on the adjoining site has an identical elevation to the one in question, and is at the same distance from the common boundary; and

(e) that no significant radiation will pass through any parts of the external wall that have fire resistance.

It may sometimes be advantageous to construct compartments of a smaller size than indicated by B3, or to provide compartments where none would otherwise be necessary, in order to reduce the separation distance (or to increase the amount of unprotected area in the wall without increasing the separation distance).

Boundaries

4.2.2 The use of the distance to a boundary rather than to another building in measuring the separation distance makes it possible to calculate the allowable proportion of unprotected areas, even where another building does not exist but may do.

A wall should be treated as facing a boundary if it makes an angle with it of 80° or less (see Diagram 25).

Usually only the distance to the boundary of the site needs to be considered. The meaning of the term boundary is explained in Diagram 25.

Notional Boundaries

4.2.3 In some circumstances the distances to other buildings on the same site needs to be considered. This should be done by assuming a boundary called a notional boundary between those buildings.

The concept of a notional boundary between two buildings on the same site and the rules that apply are illustrated in Diagram 26.

In general, it is not necessary to consider the separation distance between buildings on the same site unless one of the buildings, whether new or existing, is of Residential (Purpose Groups 1(a), 1(b), 1(c), 2(a), 2(b)) or Assembly and Recreation (Purpose Group 5) use.

Where a number of buildings of any purpose group occupy the same site and where each building is under different ownership, tenancy or occupancy or where sub-division of the site is likely to occur, it would in these circumstances be appropriate to consider space separation between all buildings on the same site.

Where buildings of any purpose group occur on the same site and where space separation has not been considered, then it is necessary to take into account the compartmentation requirements under Section B3 (3.2) as if they were connected together as one building.

Space separation between opposing elevations of the same building (see 3.2.5.9) may also need to be considered. The principles contained in this Section are also relevant to these situations.

Relevant Boundaries

4.2.4 The boundary which a wall faces whether it is the boundary of the site or a notional boundary is called the relevant boundary (see Diagrams 25 and 26).

Unprotected Areas and Fire Resistance

4.2.5 Any part of an external wall which has less fire resistance than the appropriate amount indicated in Table A1(5) and Table A2 of Appendix A is considered to be an unprotected area.

Status of Combustible Surfaces as Unprotected Area

4.2.6 Besides the restrictions on combustible surfaces in 4.1, their extent may also be limited by the result of the calculation of unprotected area if they are more than 1 mm in thickness.

Diagram 25 **Relevant boundary** *Par. 4.0.2*

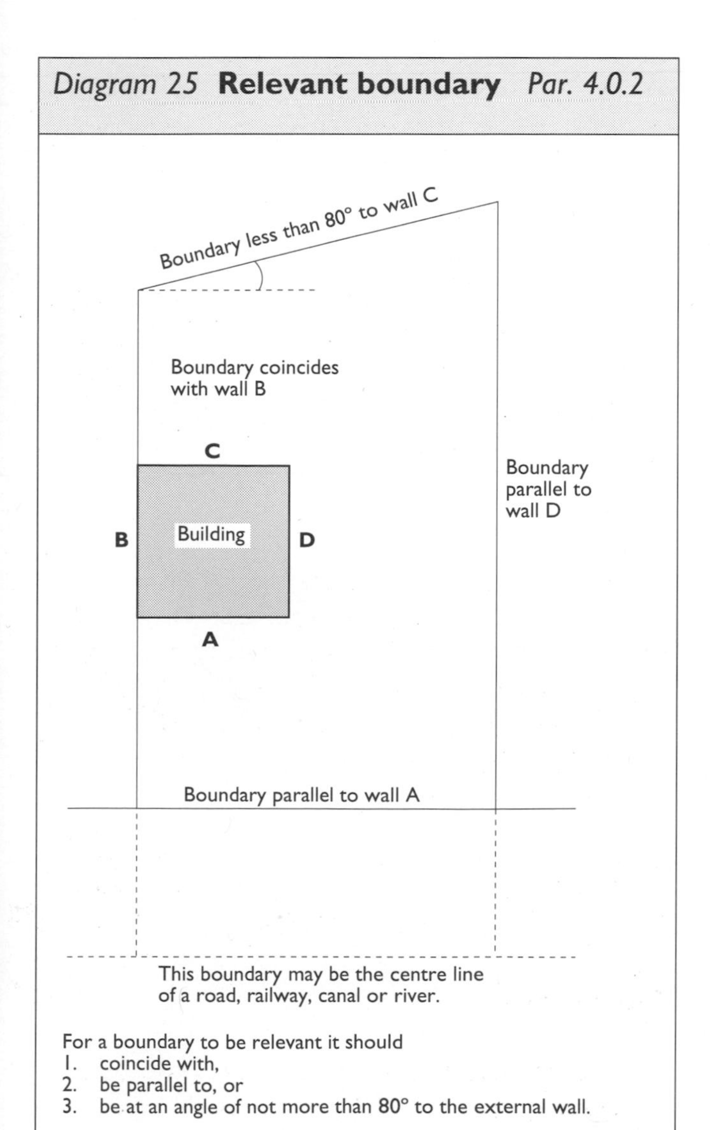

For a boundary to be relevant it should
1. coincide with,
2. be parallel to, or
3. be at an angle of not more than 80° to the external wall.

(a) If the combustible material is used as a surface on a wall that has the necessary fire resistance, then half of the area of combustible material should be counted as unprotected area.

(b) If the combustible material is used as a surface on a wall that does not have the necessary fire resistance, then the whole of the area of combustible material is counted as unprotected area.

External Walls Within 1 m of the Relevant Boundary

4.2.7 A wall situated within 1 m from any point on the relevant boundary will meet the provisions for space separation if:

(a) the only unprotected areas are those shown in Diagram 27, and

(b) the rest of the wall is fire-resisting from both sides.

External Walls 1 m or more from the Relevant Boundary

4.2.8 A wall situated at least 1 m from any point on the relevant boundary will meet the provisions for space separation if:

(a) the extent of unprotected area does not exceed that given by one of the methods referred to in 4.2.8.1 below, and

(b) the rest of the wall (if any) is fire-resisting.

Diagram 26 **Notional boundary** *Pars. 4.0.2 and 4.2.3*

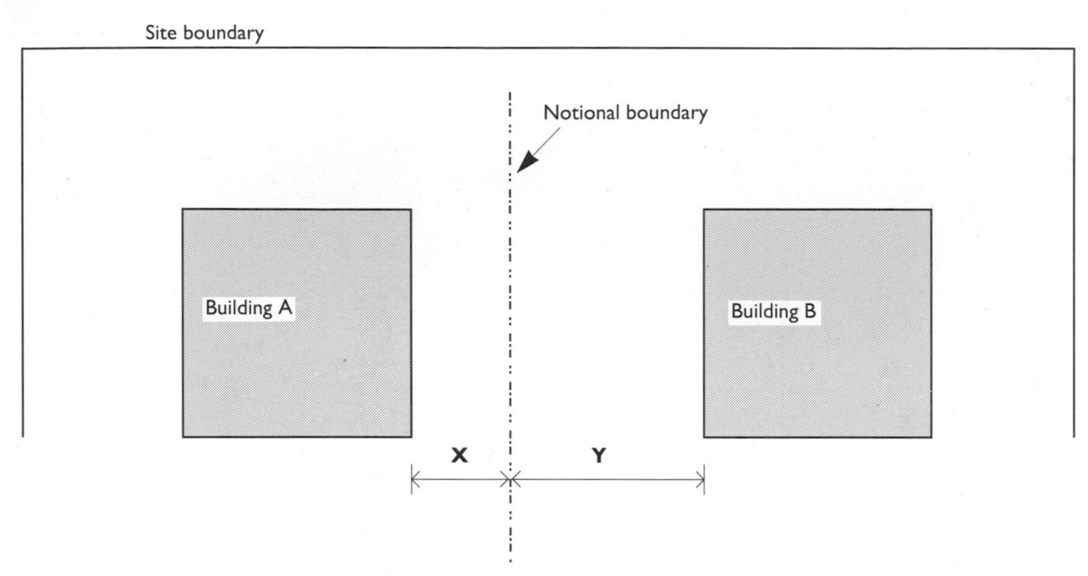

The notional boundary should be set in the area between the two buildings according to the following rules:

1. These rules only apply when two or more buildings are on the same site and when one of the buildings (new or existing) is of residential or assembly use.
2. A notional boundary should be set between a building of a use given in Rule 1 and another building of any use.
3. An existing building should be taken as if it was a new building of the same use but having the existing unprotected area and fire-resistance on the outside wall facing the notional boundary.
4. The notional boundary should be so situated that all buildings comply with the provisions for space separation, having regard to the amount of unprotected areas.
5. When set the notional boundary becomes the relevant boundary.

Dimension **X** : Compliance with the provisions for space separation in respect of Building A (in accordance with pars. 4.2.7 and 4.2.8)

Dimension **Y** : Compliance with the provisions for space separation in respect of Building B (in accordance with pars. 4.2.7 and 4.2.8)

4.2.8.1 Methods for calculating acceptable unprotected area - Two methods are given in this Document for calculating the acceptable amount of unprotected area in an external wall that is at least 1 m from any point on the relevant boundary (for walls within 1 m of the boundary see 4.2.7 above).

Method 1 (see 4.2.8.4) is only suitable for small residential buildings which do not belong to Purpose Group 2(a), Residential (Institutional).

Method 2 (see 4.2.8.5) may be used for buildings or compartments for which Method 1 is not appropriate.

Other methods are described in the Building Research Establishment Report (BR 187) "External fire spread: building separation and boundary distances".

The methods outlined in the BRE report are based on the following:

- enclosing rectangle (geometric method);
- aggregate notional areas (protractor method); and
- a calculation method (Part 2 of BRE Report)

The calculation method, which takes into account a number of fire parameters, including fire-load densities and ventilation conditions, may be the most appropriate in certain critical situations. Fire load densities may be determined by consideration of the intended use of the building, including any likely variations in fire load with time.

Diagram 27 **Unprotected areas which may be disregarded for space separation purposes** *Par. 4.2.7*

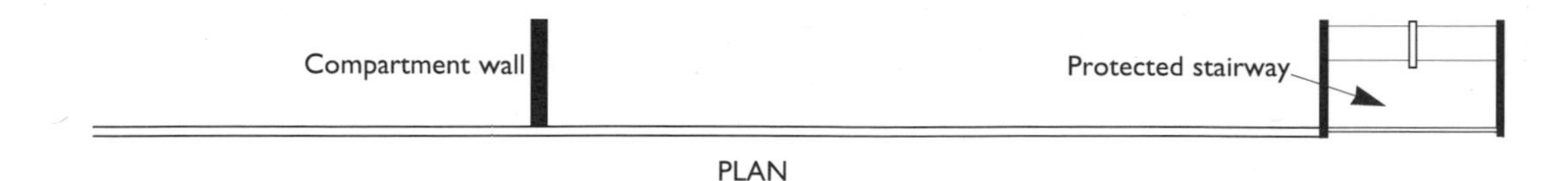

PLAN

Line of compartment wall

1.5 m min

1.5 m min

4m min

1.5m min

1.5 m min

4m min

1.5m min

Line of compartment floor

4m min

4m min

4m min

1.5 m min

1.5 m min

ELEVATION

KEY

■ Unprotected area of 0.1m² maximum

Unprotected area of 1m² maximum; or group of unprotected areas within an area of 1m x 1m

Unprotected area of external wall to protected stairway

NOTES:

(a) The unprotected area of the enclosure to a protected stairway may be disregarded for the purpose of space separation.

(b) There are restrictions in section B1 (see 1.3.6.6 and Diagram 7) on the unprotected areas of external enclosures to a building adjacent to any unprotected area in the enclosure to a protected stairway.

(c) There are also restrictions in section B1 (see 1.3.9 and Diagram 8) on unprotected areas adjacent to external escape stairways.

Dimensions shown are minimum separation distances between unprotected areas of limited size if those areas are to be disregarded for space separation purposes.

4.2.8.2 Basis for calculating acceptable unprotected area - The basis of methods 1 and 2 is set out in Fire Research Technical Paper No. 5 (1963). This has been reprinted as part of the BRE Report referred to in 4.2.8.1 above. The aim is to ensure that the building is separated from the boundary by at least half the distance at which the total thermal radiation intensity emitted from all unprotected areas in the wall would be 12.6 kW/m^2 (in still air) assuming the radiation intensity at each unprotected area is:

(a) 84 kW/m^2, if the building is in the residential, office or assembly or Recreation purpose groups, and

(b) 168 kW/m^2, if the building is in the shop, commercial, industrial, storage or other non-residential purpose groups.

4.2.8.3 Sprinkler systems - It may be assumed that the intensity of radiation from a fire in a compartment which is fitted throughout with a sprinkler system will be half the values given in 4.2.8.2 (a) and (b) above. The sprinkler system should meet the relevant recommendations of BS 5306 : Part 2 : 1990, i.e. the relevant occupancy rating together with the additional requirements for life safety.

4.2.8.4 Method 1 - small residential buildings - This method applies only to a building intended to be used as a dwelling house, or for flats or other residential purposes (not Institutional), which is not less than 1 m from any point on the relevant boundary.

The following rules for determining the maximum permitted unprotected area should be read with Diagram 28 and Table 4.2:

1. The building should not exceed 3 storeys in height (basements not counted) or be more than 24 m in length.

2. Each side of the building will meet the provisions for space separation if:

   (a) the distance of the side of the building from the relevant boundary, and

   (b) the extent of unprotected area,

   are within the limits given in Table 4.2.

Note: In calculating the maximum permitted unprotected area, any areas shown in Diagram 27 can be disregarded.

3. Any parts of the side of the building in excess of the maximum permitted unprotected area should be fire-resisting.

Diagram 28 **Small residential building** *Par. 4.2.8.4*

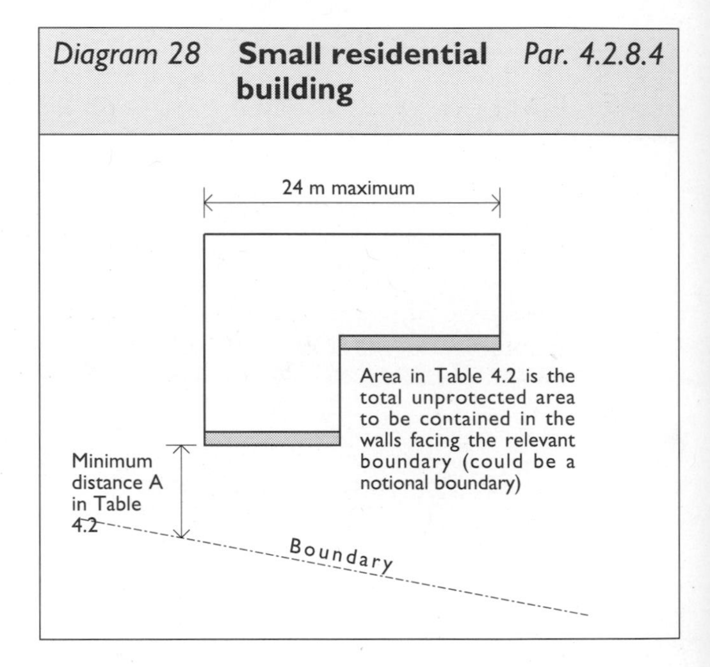

Table 4.2 **Permitted unprotected areas in small residential buildings**

Minimum distance (A) between side of building and relevant boundary(m)	Maximum total area of unprotected areas (m^2)
1.0	5.6
2.0	12
3.0	18
4.0	24
5.0	30
6.0	no limit

4.2.8.5 Method 2 - Other buildings or compartments - This method applies to a building or compartment intended for any use and not less than 1 m from any point on the relevant boundary. The following rules for determining the maximum permitted unprotected area should be read with Table 4.3.

(1) Except for open sided car parks in Purpose Group 7(b), the building or compartment should not exceed 10 m in height.

Note: For any building or compartment more than 10 m in height, the methods set out in the BRE Report 'Building separation and boundary distances' can be applied.

(2) Each side of the building will meet the provisions for space separation if:

(a) the distance of the side of the building from the relevant boundary, and

(b) the extent of unprotected area,

are within the limits of unprotected area.

Note: In calculating the maximum permitted unprotected area, any areas shown in Diagram 27 can be disregarded.

(3) Any parts of the side of the building in excess of the maximum permitted unprotected area should be fire-resisting.

Material Alteration of Existing Buildings

4.2.9 In the case of a material alteration of an existing building, the requirements in relation to space separation may be met where:

- there is no increase in the extent of unprotected areas to the existing external walls of the building; and

- the building is not altered or extended by the provision of additional floor area(s).

Table 4.3 **Permitted unprotected areas in small buildings or compartments**

Minimum distance between side of building and relevant boundary(m)		Maximum total per cent of unprotected areas (%)
Purpose Groups		
Residential, Office, Assembly and Recreation (Purpose Groups 1(a), 1(b), 1(c), 2(a), 2(b), 3 and 5)	Shop, Shopping Centre Industrial, Storage & other Non-residential (Purpose Group 4, 4(a), 6, 7 and 8)	
0	0	0
2.5	5	20
5.0	10	40
7.5	15	60
10.0	20	80
12.5	25	100

Notes

- Intermediate values may be obtained by interpolation.
- For buildings which are fitted throughout with an appropriate automatic sprinkler system meeting the relevant recommendations of BS 5306: Part 2: 1990 Fire extinguishing installations and equipment on premises, Part 2, Specification for sprinkler systems, i.e. the relevant occupancy rating together with additional requirements for life safety, the values in columns (1) and (2) may be halved.
- In the case of open sided car parks in Purpose Group 7(b) the distances set out in column (1) may be used instead of those in column (2).

Material Change of Use of Existing Buildings

4.2.10 In the case of a material change of use of an existing building the requirements in relation to space separation may be met where:

- there is no increase in the extent of un-protected areas to the existing external walls of the building; and

- the building is not altered or extended by the provision of additional floor area(s); and

- the new use will not result in an increased fire load density (i.e. the amount of combustible materials from contents and the construction, per unit floor area) in any part of the building.

Where any of the above criteria are not met, it will be necessary to demonstrate that the unprotected areas comply with the requirements outlined at 4.2.7 and 4.2.8.

Where it is necessary to increase the extent of unprotected areas of a wall on an existing elevation, it may be appropriate to employ insulated fire-resisting glazing in fixed frames or provide other fire resisting construction remote from any existing openings, to provide the necessary insulation protection.

4.3. Roof Coverings

Introduction

4.3.1 The provisions in this sub-section limit the proximity to the boundary of those types of roof covering which will not give adequate protection against the spread of fire.

Other Controls on Roofs

4.3.2 There are provisions concerning the fire properties of roofs elsewhere. In B3, there are provisions in sub-section 3.2 for roofs that pass over the top of a compartment wall or separating wall. In B2, there are provisions for the internal surfaces of rooflights as part of the internal lining of a room or circulation space.

Classification of Performance

4.3.3 The performance of roof coverings is designated by reference to the test methods specified in BS 476: Part 3: 1958, as described in Appendix A. The notional performance of some common roof coverings is given in Table A5 of Appendix A.

Rooflights are controlled on a similar basis, although there is a different method of classification for plastic rooflights.

Separation Distances

4.3.4 The separation distance is the minimum distance from the roof (or part of the roof) in question to the nearest boundary, which may be a notional boundary.

Table 4.4 sets out separation distances according to the type of roof covering and the size and use of the building. However, there are no restrictions on the use of roof coverings designated AA, AB or AC.

Plastic Rooflights

4.3.5 Table 4.5 sets out the limitations on the use of plastic rooflights which do not meet the basic provisions described in Table 4.4 but which have a lower surface of thermoplastic material with a TP(a) rigid or TP(b) classification (see A14 of Appendix A).

When used in rooflights, a rigid thermoplastic sheet product made from polycarbonate or from unplasticised PVC, which achieves a Class 1 rating for surface flame spread when tested to BS 476 Part 7, 1971 or 1987, can be regarded as having an AA designation.

Glass in Rooflights

4.3.6 When used in rooflights, unwired glass at least 4 mm thick can be regarded as having an AA designation. Thinner glass should only be used where the separation distance is 6 m or more, unless the glass is over one of the following:

(a) a balcony, verandah, open carport, covered way, loading bay or detached swimming pool; or

(b) a garage, conservatory or outbuilding, with a maximum floor area of 40 m^2.

Table 4.4 **Limitations on roof coverings***				
Designation of covering of roof, or part of roof	**Minimum distance from any point on relevant boundary**			
	Less than 6m	**At least 6m**	**At least 12m**	**At least 20m**
AA, AB or AC	√	√	√	√
BA, BB or BC	x	√	√	√
CA, CB or CC	x	√ (1)	√ (2)	√
AD, BD or CD	x	√ (1)	√ (2)	√ (2)
DA, DB, DC or DD	x	x	x	√ (1)
thatch or wood shingles (3)	x	√ (1)	√ (2)	√ (2)

Notes:

* See par. 4.3.6 for limitation on glass and Table 4.5 for limitation on plastic rooflights.

√ - Acceptable

x - Not acceptable

√(1) Not acceptable on any building listed below:

(a) houses in terraces of three or more houses;

(b) industrial, storage or other non-residential purpose group buildings of any size; and

(c) any other buildings with a cubic capacity of more than 1500 m^3.

and only acceptable on other buildings if the part of the roof is no more than 3 m^2 area and is at least 1.5 m from any similar part, with the roof between the parts covered with a material of limited combustibility.

√(2) Not acceptable on any of the buildings listed at (a), (b) or (c) in (1) above.

(3) Where the performance under BS 476: Part 3: 1958 cannot be established..

Table 4.5 **Limitations on plastic rooflights**				
Classification on lower surface (1)	Space which rooflight can serve	Minimum distance from any point on relevant boundary to rooflight with an external surface classification (2) of:		
		TP(a)	TP(b)	DA DB DC DD
1. TP(a) rigid	any space except a protected stairway	6 m (3)	6 m (5)	20 m
2. TP(b)	(a) balcony, verandah, carport, covered way or loading bay, which has at least one longer side wholly or permanently open (b) detached swimming pool (c) conservatory, garage or outbuilding, with a maximum floor area of 40 m^2	6 m	6 m	20 m
	(d) circulation space (4) (except a protected stairway) (e) room (4)	6 m (5)	6 m (5)	20 m (5)

Notes:

(1) See also the guidance to B2.

(2) The classification of external roof surfaces is explained in Appendix A.

(3) No limit in the case of any space described in 2a, b and c.

(4) Single skin rooflight only, in the case of non-thermoplastic material.

(5) The rooflight should also meet the provisions of Diagram 29.

None of the above designations are suitable for protected stairways - (see 2.3.3).
Products may have upper and lower surfaces with different properties if they have double skins or are laminates of different materials.

Diagram 29 **Limits on spacing and size of plastic rooflights having a TP(b) lower surface** *Table 4.5*

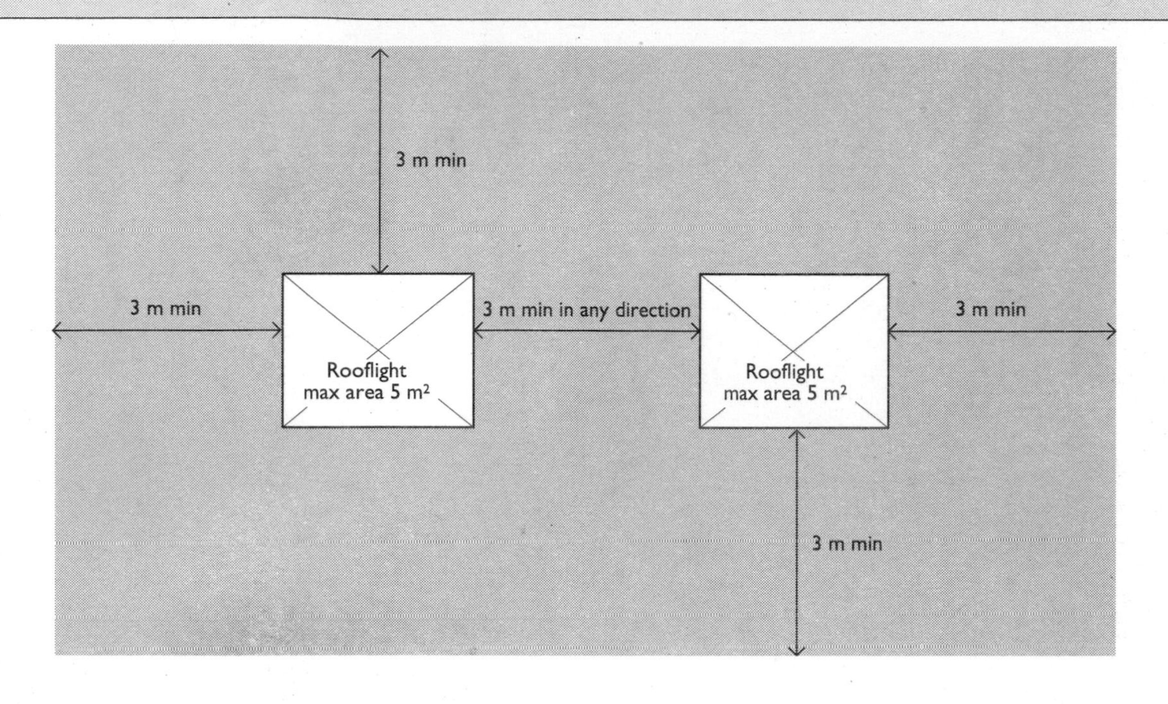

KEY

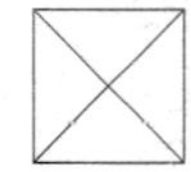

Rooflight or group of rooflights not exceeding 5 m^2

Roof covering to be a material of limited combustibility

Section B5
Access and Facilities for the Fire Service

Access and facilities for the fire service.	**B5**	A building shall be so designed and constructed that there is adequate provision for access for fire appliances and for such other facilities as may be reasonably required to assist the fire service in the protection of life and property.

Performance

The requirement of B5 may be met:

(a) if there is sufficient means of external access to enable fire appliances to be brought near to the building for effective use;

(b) if there is sufficient means of access into, and within, the building for fire-fighting personnel to effect rescue and fight fire; and

(c) if the building is provided with sufficient fire mains and other facilities to assist firefighters in their tasks;

all to an extent dependent on the use and size of the building.

Contents

5.0 Introduction to Provisions

Scope

5.0.1 While the fire safety objectives of Part B relate principally to the protection of life from fire (see 0.3.8), Section B5 relates to measures intended to assist the fire services in the protection of life and property from fire.

Fire authorities have functions under the Fire Services Act, 1981 to provide fire brigades for the extinguishment of fires and for the protection and rescue of persons and property from injury by fire. Regulation B5 provides for the provision of access and other facilities to assist the fire service in the protection of life and property from fire.

The guidance in this Section relates to the provision of facilities for the fire service within and around buildings for the purpose of protecting life and mitigating property damage due to fire.

To assist the fire service some or all of the following facilities may be necessary, depending mainly on the size of the building:

- vehicle access to the building for fire appliances;
- access to and within the building for fire fighting personnel;
- fire mains around and within buildings, including the provision of hydrants;
- provisions for venting of heat and smoke from basement areas and other spaces;
- other facilities such as foam inlets to basement boiler-houses and fuel storage and electrical isolation switches.

Factors Determining Facilities Appropriate to a Specific Building

5.0.2 The main factor determining the facilities needed to assist the fire service is the size of the building.

The facilities provided also depend on the expected method of fire fighting; whether this will be from outside or inside the building. The following considerations will determine the extent of the facilities required for any particular situation:

(a) In many instances fire fighting is carried out within the building. In deep basements and tall buildings fire fighters will invariably work inside. They need special access facilities (see sub-section 5.3), equipped with fire mains, as described in sub-section 5.1. Fire appliances need access to entry points near the fire mains, as described in sub-section 5.2.

(b) In other buildings the combination of personnel access facilities offered by the normal means of escape, and the ability to work from ladders and appliances on the perimeter is sufficient without special internal arrangements. Depending on the size of the building, vehicle access may be needed to some or all of the perimeter, as explained in sub-section 5.2.

(c) Access for personnel to basement areas may in particular present difficulties, as the products of combustion from a fire tend to escape by way of the stairways. This problems can be reduced by the provision of ventilation. Ventilation may also be appropriate in other situations, particularly from large spaces within buildings. Venting can improve visibility and reduce temperatures, thus assisting search, rescue and fire fighting. Guidance on ventilation for fire fighting is indicated in 5.4.3.

(d) Water is the normal extinguishing medium for fire within buildings. Water is obtained in the first instance from the supplies carried on the first responding fire appliances. This is supplemented with water from public mains or fire mains on the site, where available, or pumped from other adjacent sources such as rivers, canals, ponds or static storage tanks, where provided. Water may also be ferried by water-carrying tankers or relayed by pumping from remote sources. Guidance on the provision of fire mains is given in sub-section 5.1.

(e) Certain areas, such as boiler rooms and fuel storage areas within buildings require special provisions, such as facilities for pumping foam extinguishing medium from outside. Other facilities may be required to isolate electrical supplies, particularly in the case of high voltage installations. Guidance on these special provisions is contained in sub-section 5.4.

Existing Buildings

5.0.3 In the case of a material alteration of an existing building, the requirements of B5 of the Second Schedule to the Building Regulations may be met:

(i) if the access and facilities for the fire service are not altered in such a way as to reduce the extent or performance of those that existed before the material alteration; and

(ii) if the building is not extended or altered by the addition of floor area at any level or the subject of a material change of use.

In the case of a material change of use of a building, it will be necessary to assess the access and facilities for the fire services in accordance with the guidance of the relevant sub-section to this Section. However, in relation to vehicle access, special provisions are made for existing buildings (see 5.2.3). It may also be prudent to seek advice from the relevant fire authority in relation to such matters.

Definitions

5.0.4 The following definitions apply specifically to B5. Other terms applicable more widely throughout this Document are given in Appendix D.

Firefighting lift: a lift designed to have additional protection, with controls that enable it to be used under the direct control of the fire brigade in fighting a fire.

Firefighting lobby: a protected lobby for providing access from a firefighting stairway to the accommodation area and to any associated firefighting lift.

Firefighting shaft: a protected shaft containing a firefighting stairway, firefighting lobbies and, if provided, a firefighting lift.

Firefighting stairway: a protected stairway communicating with the accommodation area only through a firefighting lobby.

Fire mains: pipes installed in and around buildings and equipped so that the fire service may connect hoses to receive a supply of water for fire fighting.

Hydrant: an assembly comprising a valve and outlet connection from an external fire mains, provided to deliver a supply of water for fire-fighting.

Perimeter (of buildings): The maximum aggregate plan perimeter, formed by vertical projection onto a horizontal plane but excluding any parts which are connected to adjoining buildings (see Diagram 31).

5.1. Fire Mains

Introduction

5.1.1 Fire mains are pipes installed in and around a building and equipped so that the fire service may connect hoses to receive a supply of water to fight fires. Fire mains are divided into two types as follows:

- internal fire mains (see 5.1.2); and

- external fire mains and hydrants (see 5.1.7, 5.1.8).

Provision of Internal Fire Mains

5.1.2 Internal fire mains may be of two types:

- rising mains, serving floors above ground or access level; or

- falling mains serve levels below ground or access level.

Internal fire mains may also be of the "dry" type which are normally empty and are supplied through hose from a fire service pumping appliance, or they may be of the "wet" type kept full of water and supplied from tanks and pumps in the building.

Internal fire mains should be provided in all buildings where a firefighting shaft is also required (see 5.3). The following provisions are required for the situations as described:

(a) in buildings with a floor at more than 20 m above ground level, storeys above ground level should be equipped with wet or dry rising fire mains;

(b) in buildings with a basement at more than 10 m below ground level, basement storeys should be equipped with wet or dry fire mains;

(c) in buildings with any floor at more than 60 m above ground level, storeys above ground level should be equipped with wet rising fire mains.

Number and Location of Internal Fire Mains

5.1.3 Where internal fire mains are installed, they should be positioned so that at each level other than ground level there is one main for every firefighting shaft provided to meet the provisions in paragraph 5.3.3.

If there are no firefighting shafts but internal fire mains are to be installed, the criteria in par. 5.3.3 for the number and location of firefighting shafts may be used to determine the provision of internal fire mains, even though the building may not have a storey at more than 20 m above ground level.

5.1.4 The outlets from internal fire mains should be sited in:

(a) a firefighting shaft (see sub-section 5.3), or

(b) a protected stairway, or

(c) a balcony or walkway in the open air.

Design and Construction of Internal Fire Mains

5.1.5 The design and construction of internal fire mains should be in accordance with the relevant sections of BS 5306: Part 1: 1988 (excluding clause 6).

Sources of Water for Firefighting

5.1.6 Water for firefighting is available by way of a number of possible sources as follows:

(a) Water carried on fire appliances (water tenders, water tankers, etc.);

(b) Hydrants on external fire mains;

(c) Static storage tanks or reservoirs where provided;

(d) Other sources such as rivers, canals, ponds, etc., where adequate access for pumping is available.

Provision of Hydrants

5.1.7 The following buildings should be provided with one or more external fire hydrants, complying with the requirements of BS 750: 1984 Specification for underground fire hydrants and surface box frames and covers, and with any specific requirements of the relevant fire authority:

- every building provided with an internal fire main, wet or dry;

- every building having a floor area on any storey of more than 1000 m^2;

For buildings, or groups of buildings, exceeding 1000 m^2 in ground floor area, at least one hydrant should be provided for every 1000 m^2 of the area covered at ground level.

Fire hydrants should be located as shown in Diagram 30 and such that:

- the distance from the building is not less than 6 m or more than 46 m;

- the distance from a hydrant to a vehicle access roadway or hard-standing area for fire appliances (see 5.2) is not more than 30 m;

- they are distributed around the perimeter of the building, having regard to the provision of access for fire appliances (see 5.2): and

- the hydrants are located on the same site as the building or are provided by a sanitary authority on a public roadway adjacent to the site.

A hydrant situated inside a building may also be acceptable where it is:

Diagram 30 **External fire mains and hydrants** *Par. 5.1.7*

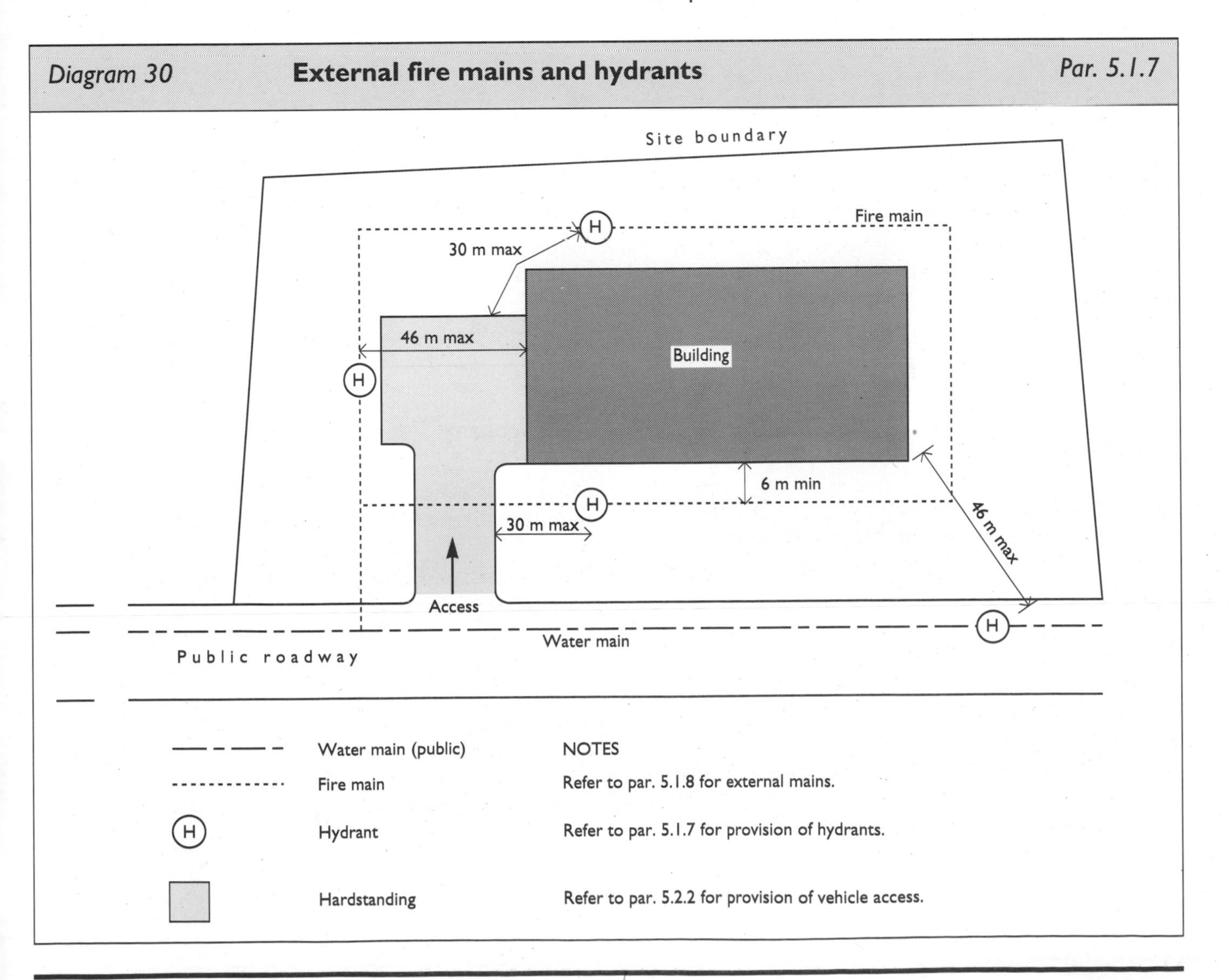

- in a separate fire compartment i.e. separated from the rest of the building by compartment walls;

- not more than 4.5 m and visible from an entrance to the building; and

- indicated by a suitable notice at the entrance.

All hydrants should be conspicuously marked in accordance with BS 3251: 1976 Specification of indicator plates for fire hydrants and emergency water supplies.

External Fire Mains

5.1.8 Most urban areas are supplied with water through public water mains. Where such mains are provided it is normal to have hydrants provided for the fire brigade to obtain a ready supply of water for firefighting. The siting of these hydrants is important both from the point of view of accessibility for fire brigade use and proximity to buildings for quick and effective firefighting (see 5.1.7).

The provision of water mains, and suitably located hydrants outside of the site of a building does not come within the scope of the Building Regulations.

In many cases, especially for smaller developments in urban areas, hydrants on public water mains will be adequate. However, for larger buildings, the hydrants available from the public mains outside of the site may not be sufficient for firefighting. In these situations, hydrants on external fire mains within the site of the building will provide the most convenient source of water. This source may be supplemented by hydrants on public mains or other sources indicated at 5.1.6.

Where required to provide hydrants in accordance with 5.1.7, fire mains should be designed to be capable of providing satisfactory flows and pressures. Guidance for the design of hydrant systems is contained in BS 5306: Part 1: 1976. For improved and more reliable supplies, external fire mains on a site should preferably be installed as part of a ring main system.

5.2. Vehicle Access

Introduction

5.2.1 Fire brigade vehicle access to the exterior of a building is required to enable high reach appliances, such as turntable ladders and hydraulic platforms, to be deployed, and to enable pumping appliances to supply water and equipment for firefighting.

Access requirements increase with building size and height and also depend on whether the building is fitted with internal fire mains (see 5.1).

Access for fire appliances should be provided in accordance with the provisions outlined in 5.2.2. below.

Vehicle access routes and hard-standings should meet the criteria described in 5.2.4 if they are to be used by fire service vehicles.

Provision of Vehicle Access

5.2.2 For effective firefighting operations, fire brigade appliances should be able to get within easy reach of a building. For small buildings it is generally only necessary to have access to one external elevation, but larger buildings will require access to all or a number of elevations.

Vehicle access should be provided in accordance with the criteria indicated in Table 5.1. Any elevation to which vehicle access is provided in accordance with Table 5.1 should contain a door giving access to the interior of the building.

In the case of a building fitted with a dry internal fire main, access for a pump appliance should be provided to within 18 m and within sight of the inlet connection point.

In the case of a building fitted with a wet internal fire main, access for a pump appliance should be provided to within 18 m and within sight of an entrance giving access to the main and within sight of the inlet connection to the suction tank for the main.

In the case of a building which has adjoining buildings on one or more sides, the perimeter (see 5.0.4 and Diagram 31 for the definition of 'perimeter') which is available to provide access is less than for a free-standing building. Where there are adjoining buildings on more than two sides, the access requirement derived from Table 5.1 may not therefore be adequate. In these situations it may be appropriate to consult with the relevant fire authority in relation to access and other facilities or compensating features as are considered necessary.

In the provision of access for fire appliances, consideration should also be given to the position of any hydrants required by reason of the criteria outlined in 5.1.

Existing Buildings

5.2.3 In the case of existing buildings, where access for fire appliances is not in accordance with the provisions outlined at 5.2.2, it is appropriate to consider a range of compensating measures, depending on the circumstances of each particular case. Such measures could include additional personnel access (see 5.3) to the building for firefighting, additional internal fire mains (see 5.1) and other facilities to assist firefighting.

In the case of an existing small building, with a total floor area of up to 1000 m^2 where the height of the top storey is under 10 m, access for fire service pump appliances should generally be provided to within 45 m of the principal entrance to the building.

In large or complex buildings it will be necessary to provide access to within a reasonable distance of a number of points on the exterior and to within a reasonable distance of other entry points to the building. In these cases it may be appropriate to consult with the relevant fire authority in this regard.

Table 5.1	**Vehicle access to buildings**		
Volume of building (m^3)	**Height of top storey above ground (m)**	**Provide vehicle access**	**Type of appliance**
up to 7,000	under 10	at rate of 2.4 m in length for every 90 m^2 of ground floor area	pump
	over 10	to 15% of perimeter	high reach
7,000-28,000	up to 10 over 10	to 15% of perimeter to 50% of perimeter	pump high reach
28,500-56,000	up to 10 over 10	to 50% of perimeter to 50% of perimeter	pump high reach
56,000-85,000	up to 10 over 10	to 75% of perimeter to 75% of perimeter	pump high reach
over 85,000	up to 10 over 10	to 100% of perimeter to 100% of perimeter	pump high reach

Note: See 5.0.4 and Diagram 31 for the definition of 'perimeter'.

Design of Access Routes and Hard-standings

5.2.4 A vehicle access route may be a public or private road, or other route, which, including any manhole or other covers, meets the standards in Table 5.2, Diagram 32 and the following paragraphs.

Access routes to buildings with any storey at more than 10 m above ground level should meet the standards for high reach appliances. For lower buildings the access should be to the standards for pumping appliances.

Where access is provided to an elevation in accordance with Table 5.2, overhead obstructions such as overhead cables that would interfere with the setting of ladders etc., should be avoided in the area shown on Diagram 32.

Where access roadways are provided within the site of a building, turning facilities for appliances, in accordance with the requirements of Table 5.2 should be provided in any dead-end access route that is more than 20 m long

Table 5.2	**Vehicle access route specifications**					
Appliance type	Minimum width of road between kerbs (m)	Minimum width of gateways between kerbs (m)	Minimum turning circle between kerbs (m)	Minimum turning circle between walls (m)	Minimum clearance height (m)	Minimum carrying capacity (tonnes)
Pump	3.7	3.1	16.8	19.2	3.7	12.5
High Reach	3.7	3.1	26	29	4	16.25

Note:
Use of these figures will cater for nearly all of the fire appliances in use at present. Some fire authorities use different sized appliances and it is therefore advisable that the relevant fire authority be consulted.

Diagram 31 **Building perimeter** *Table 5.1*

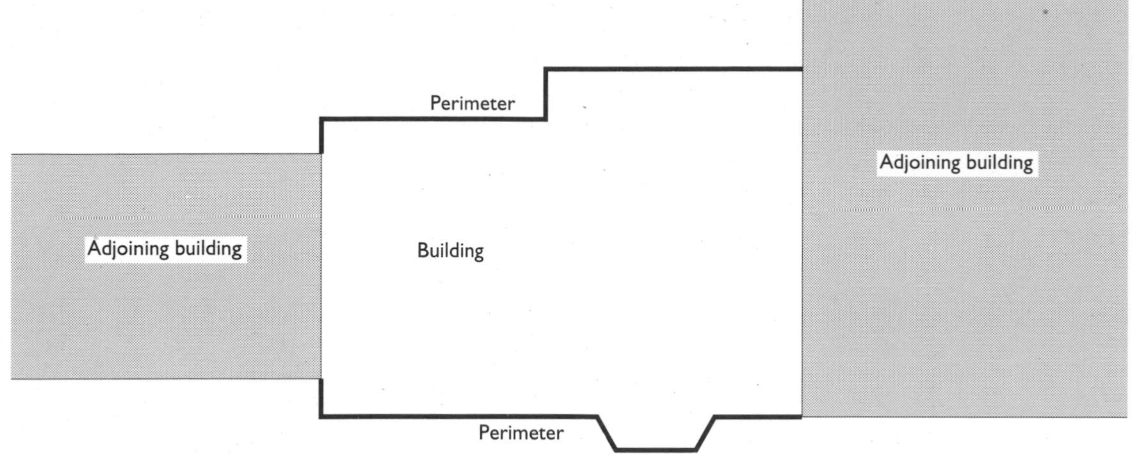

APPLICATION TO TERRACE BUILDING

1. Perimeter excludes separating walls.

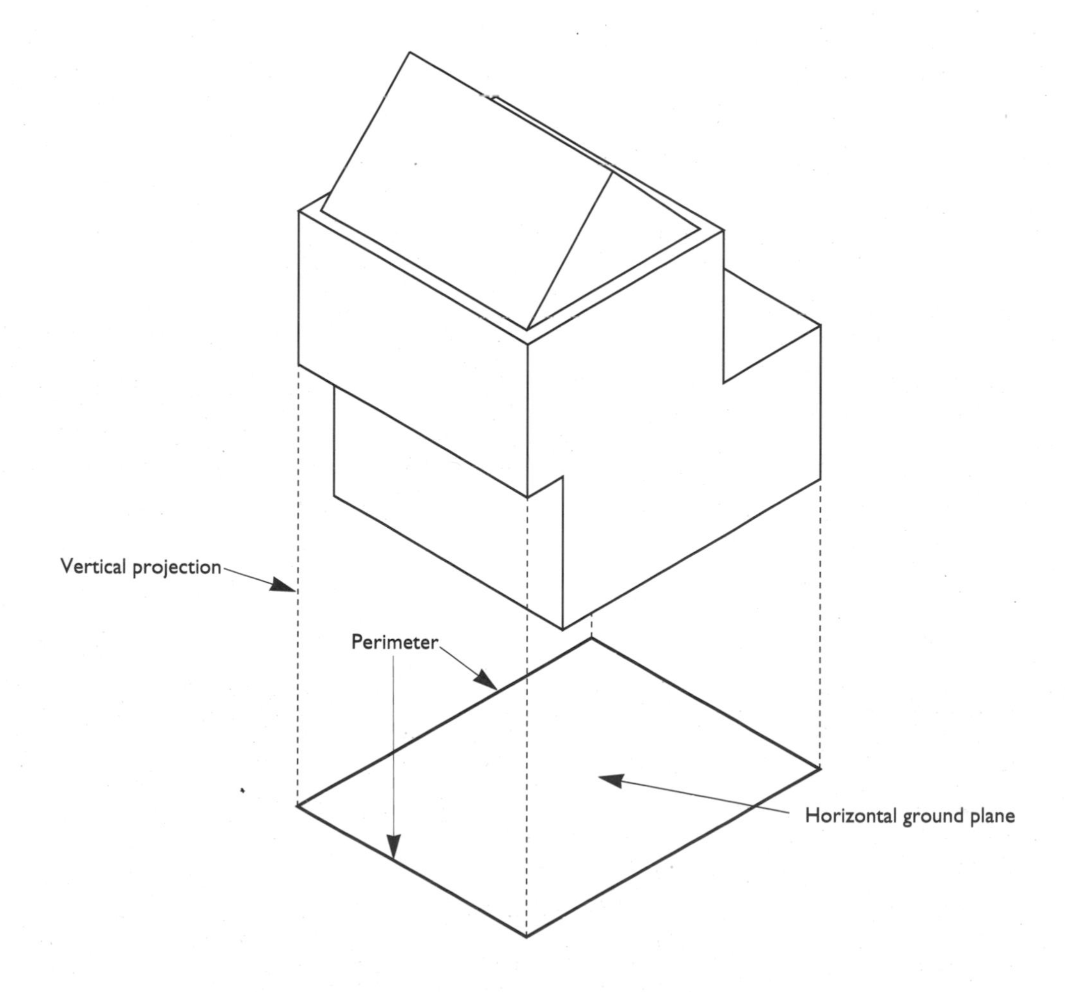

APPLICATION TO FREESTANDING BUILDING

2. Perimeter is the maximum aggregate plan perimeter found by vertical projection onto a horizontal ground plane.

Diagram 32 **Fire appliance (high reach) access to buildings** *Par. 5.2.4*

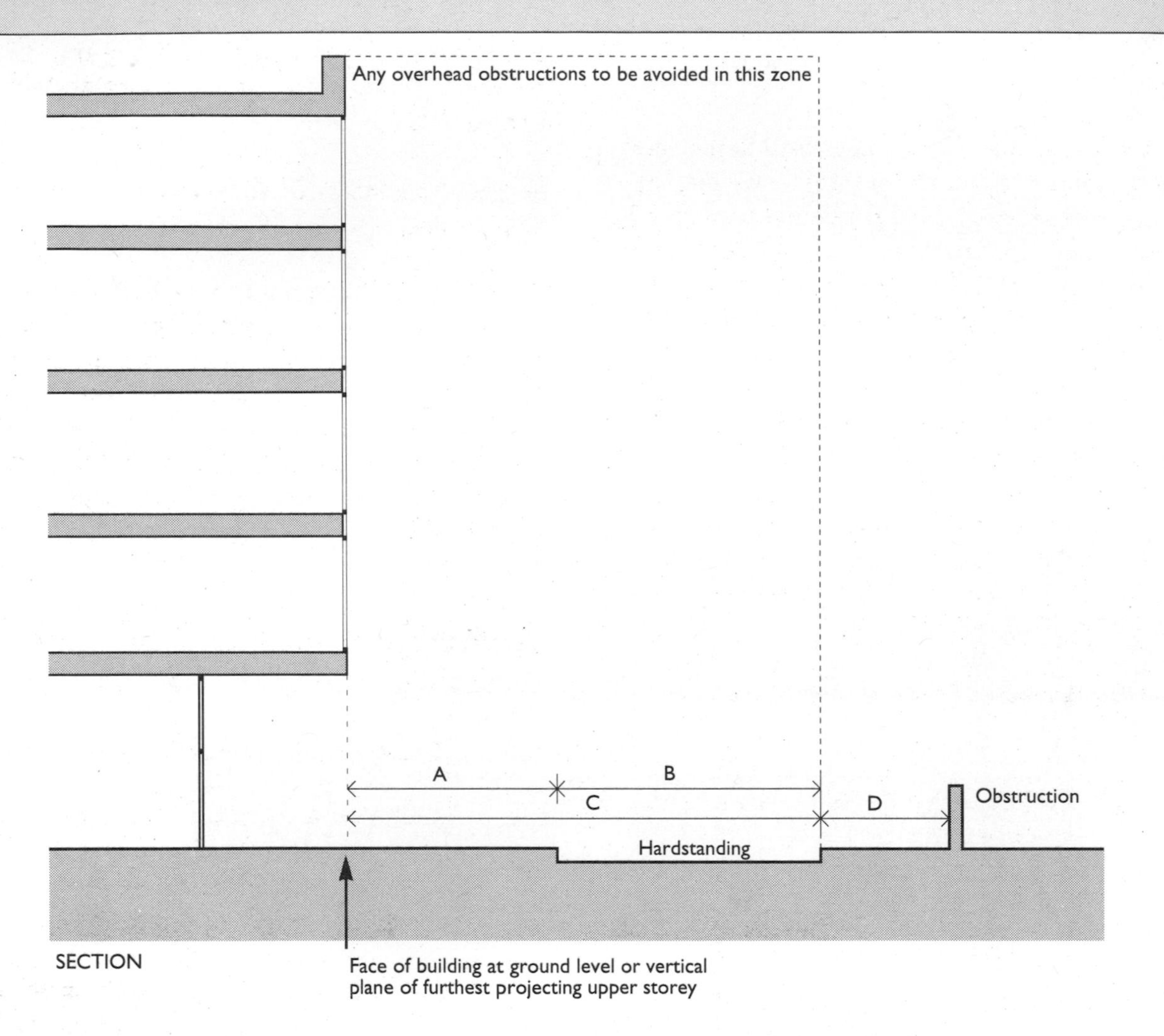

DIMENSION		TYPE OF APPLIANCE	
		Turntable ladder	Hydraulic platform
A	Max distance of hardstanding from building	4.9 m	2.0 m
B	Minimum width of hardstanding	5.0 m	5.5 m
C	Minimum distance of further edge of hardstanding	10 m	7.5 m
D	Minimum width of unobstructed space for swing of hydraulic platform	n/a	2.2 m

NOTE

Hardstanding for high reach appliances should be as level as possible and should not exceed a gradient of 1 in 12.

5.3. Personnel Access to Buildings for Firefighting

Introduction

5.3.1 In low rise buildings without deep basements fire service personnel access requirements may be met by a combination of the normal means of escape, and the measures for vehicle access in sub-section 5.2, which facilitate ladder access to upper storeys. In other buildings the problems of reaching the fire, and working inside near the fire, merit the provision of additional facilities to avoid delay and to provide a sufficiently secure operating base to allow effective action to be taken.

These additional facilities include firefighting lifts, firefighting stairways and firefighting lobbies, which are combined in a protected shaft known as the firefighting shaft (Diagram 33).

Provisions for protected shafts in general are given in Section B3.

Diagram 33 **Firefighting shaft components** (typical arrangement) *Par. 5.3.1*

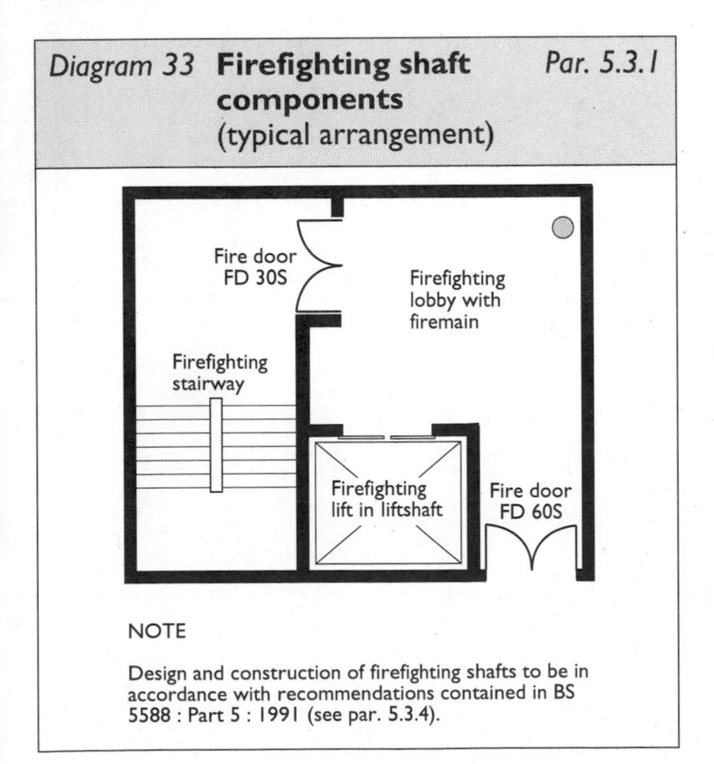

NOTE

Design and construction of firefighting shafts to be in accordance with recommendations contained in BS 5588 : Part 5 : 1991 (see par. 5.3.4).

Provision of Firefighting Shafts

5.3.2 Buildings with a floor at more than 20 m above ground level or with a basement at more than 10 m below ground level, should be provided with firefighting shafts containing firefighting lifts.

Every firefighting stairway and firefighting lift should be approached through a firefighting lobby (see Diagram 33).

A firefighting stairway should serve every storey of the building.

A firefighting lift should serve every storey above ground, including the ground floor, in a building with any floor 20 m or more above ground. However a firefighting lift need not serve a storey in a building used as flats (purpose group 1(c)) on which there is no entrance to a dwelling. A firefighting lift should also serve every storey below ground, and the ground floor, in a building with a basement at more than 10 m below ground;

Number and Location of Firefighting Shafts

5.3.3 The number of firefighting shafts should:

(a) (if the building is fitted throughout with an automatic sprinkler system meeting the relevant recommendations of BS 5306: Part 2) comply with Table 5.3; or

(b) (if the building is not fitted with sprinklers) be such that there is at least one for every 900 m^2 (or part thereof) of floor area of the largest floor that is more than 20 m above ground level.

The location of firefighting shafts should be such that every part of every storey, other than fire service access level, is no more than 60 m from the entrance to a firefighting lobby, measured on a route suitable for laying hose. If the internal layout is unknown at the design stage, then every part of every such storey should be no more than 40 m in a direct line from the entrance to a firefighting lobby.

Table 5.3 **Minimum number of firefighting shafts in buildings fitted with sprinklers**

Floor area of the largest storey over 20 m above ground level (sq. m)	Minimum number of firefighting shafts
less than 900	1
900 to 2000	2
2001 to 3500	3
over 3500	1 for every 1500 m^2 of floor area, or part thereof

Design and Construction of Firefighting Shafts

5.3.4 All firefighting shafts should be equipped with internal fire mains having outlet connections and valves in every firefighting lobby except at access level.

Firefighting shafts should be designed and installed in accordance with the recommendations of BS 5588: Part 5: 1991 Code of practice for fire-fighting stairs and lifts in respect of the following:

- planning within the firefighting shaft
- fire mains and landing valves
- smoke control
- fire resistance
- fire doors
- glazed areas
- firefighting lift installation
- electrical supply
- fire brigade communications system

Firefighting shaft walls should be of robust construction so that their fire resistance is unlikely to be impaired by mechanical damage.

5.4 Areas Requiring Special Consideration

There are a number of situations which pose particular difficulties and where additional facilities should be provided to assist the fire brigades.

Boiler Rooms and Fuel Stores

5.4.1 In buildings where the heating installation is oil-fuelled, and in particular where the oil storage tanks and oil burning equipment are situated below ground level, a fire involving the fuel and equipment can be tackled by the fire brigade using foam, introduced into the heating or storage chamber through foam inlets.

Every room which contains oil burning equipment or has storage tanks of greater capacity and situated as in Table 5.4 should be provided with a foam inlet for use by the fire brigade.

The inlet should be sited on an external wall not more than 900 mm above ground level and at least 3 m horizontally from any opening to the protected room to ensure that the fire brigade personnel are able to use the inlet without hindrance from heat and smoke which may emerge from the opening.

The pipe from its inlet coupling should have an internal diameter of 80 mm (nominal), be without acute bends and not exceed 10 m in length to the point of discharge of the foam. Inlets should be fitted with a 63.5 mm instantaneous coupling complying with BS 336: 1989.

The discharge of foam should be so arranged to impinge on a wall approximately 900 mm above the floor level of the room or 150 mm above the catchpit level, whichever is the higher.

High Voltage Discharge Lighting

5.4.2 Where high voltage discharge lighting is used inside or outside buildings, fire brigade personnel could be in considerable danger during fire fighting operations. It is therefore necessary to provide a switch, readily accessible to fire fighters, which will enable them to turn off and isolate this high voltage lighting before commencing fire fighting.

5.4.2.1 Provision of switches - One or more switches should be provided to enable the fire brigade personnel to switch off the discharge lighting in the event of a fire. Such switches are needed where exterior discharge lighting (e.g. advertising signs) and/or interior discharge lighting systems are provided. The switches should be readily accessible and conspicuously marked to enable fire fighters to switch them off without delay.

A firefighting emergency switch should be provided for:

- exterior discharge lighting installations operating at a voltage exceeding low voltage; and
- interior discharge lighting installations operating unattended at a voltage exceeding low voltage.

For the purposes of these provisions an installation in a closed market or in an arcade is considered to be an exterior installation.

Table 5.4 **Provision of foam inlets**

Situation of room	Contents	Provision of foam inlets
Wholly below ground and area greater than 45 m^2	- heating appliance(s) > 45 kW - oil storage tank(s) > 2,000 litres	One inlet per 45 m^2 of floor area of room
Accessible only from inside the building	- heating appliance(s) > 45 kW - oil storage tank(s) > 2,000 litres	One inlet per 45 m^2 of floor area of room

5.4.2.2 Requirements for switches - Every firefighting emergency switch provided should comply with all the relevant requirements of the following items (i) to (iv).

(i) For exterior installations, the switch should be outside the building and adjacent to the discharge lamp(s), or, alternatively, a notice indicating the position of the switch shall be placed adjacent to the discharge lamp(s) and a nameplate should be fixed near the switch so as to render it clearly distinguishable.

(ii) For interior installations, the switch should be in the main entrance to the building or in another position to be agreed with the local fire authority.

(iii) The switch should be placed in a conspicuous position, reasonably accessible to fire fighters and, except where otherwise agreed with the local fire authority, at not less than 2.75 m from the ground.

(iv) Where more than one switch is installed on any one building, each switch should be clearly marked to indicate the installation or part of the installation which it controls, and the local fire authority should be notified accordingly.

Note: Wherever practicable, all exterior installations on any one building should be controlled by a single fireman's switch. Similarly, all internal installations in any one building should be controlled by a single fire fighter's switch independent of the switch for any external installation.

For the purpose of the above provisions, low voltage is defined as not exceeding 1000 V a.c, or 1500 V d.c. between conductors, or 600 V a.c. or 900 d.c. between any conductor and earth.

Ventilation of Heat and Smoke

5.4.3 Ventilation of heat and smoke plays an important role in fire-fighting operations. How this can be achieved, if and when required, is generally a matter for the fire brigade. However, certain design features will assist in this regard. Fire-fighting in basement areas can present difficulties with access for personnel and in these situations ventilation which is independent of any stairways will be of assistance.

Provisions for ventilation in car parks are included in 3.5.2. These provision principally relate to the fire resistance requirements for the elements of structure, but will also assist fire-fighting.

5.4.3.1 Basements - Smoke ventilation from basements generally take the form of outlets vents connected directly to the open air. Such ventilation should be provided from every basement storey except in the following:

(a) a basement in a dwelling house (Purpose Group I(a) and I(b));

(b) a basement having an area less than 200 m^2 and a floor which is not more than 3 m below the adjacent ground level.

Smoke vents should be sited at high level and should be distributed around the building perimeter to maximise the effectiveness of cross-ventilation. The clear cross-sectional area of all smoke vents, allowing for frames and louvres, should not be less than 2.5% of the basement storey served. Where a basement is compartmented, each compartment should be ventilated separately. Generally, smoke vents from basements should be permanently open and unobstructed, but where they are readily accessible from the outside, consideration can be given to suitably indicated removable covers. Smoke vents should not be positioned where they would prevent the use of the means of escape from the building.

As an alternative to outlet vents as described above, a system of mechanical extraction may be provided, where the basement is also protected by an appropriate sprinkler system complying with BS 5306: Part 2: 1990. The ventilation system should meet the criteria set out in 3.5.2.5 and should operate automatically on activation of the sprinkler system.

5.4.3.2 Escape stairways - Smoke control in escape stairways is of assistance at the later stages in the development of a fire and will assist fire brigade operations. Smoke control is usually provided by openable windows or openable vents at the top of the enclosure. Every protected stairway enclosure should be provided with:

(i) openable windows at each upper storey or landing; or

(ii) an openable vent having clear openable area of not less than 1 m^2 situated at the top of the enclosure. This vent should be automatically opened by activation of smoke detectors in the stairway enclosure and should also be manually openable for fire brigade use.

5.4.3.3 Large undivided and windowless spaces - Large undivided floor areas can present difficult firefighting problems. The accumulation of heat and smoke in a fire may prevent access to these areas and limit the potential for rescue and effective firefighting from within the building. The provision of smoke and heat venting can greatly improve the effectiveness of such operations.

Fire extinguishment is normally accomplished by absorption of heat by water from hose streams or sprinklers. The reduction of heat build-up within the building by adequate venting facilities can reduce the amount of water required for cooling and extinguishment. However, ventilation is not a substitute for sprinklers or other extinguishing facilities. Its purpose is to release smoke and heat from the building and to improve accessibility for the fire services.

The principles described above are equally applicable to large windowless accommodation, where a fire has very limited ability to vent to the outside, and thereby giving rise to difficulties with firefighting operations.

Facilities for ventilation of smoke and heat for the purpose of assisting the fire service in the protection of life and property should be provided in single storey buildings or compartments exceeding 4,000 m^2 in area or 20,000 m^3 in cubic capacity (see Appendix C, Diagram 35) having the following uses:

- Shop (Purpose Group 4),
- Industrial (Purpose Group 6), or
- Storage (Purpose Group 7).

Ventilation facilities include roof mounted exhaust ventilators of suitable size and distribution and adequate inlet air provisions. The space below the roof generally requires division into smoke reservoirs of appropriate dimensions. Ventilation may also be provided or supplemented by the nature of the roof/building fabric, such as by the use of rooflights. It may also be possible to provide inlet air from adjacent smoke reservoirs or by means of external windows or doors. Facilities for the ventilation of heat and smoke for firefighting purposes are not generally required to operate automatically.

Guidance on the design of ventilation systems appropriate for these purposes are contained in Section 3, Chapter 9 of the Society of Fire Protection Engineers "Handbook of Fire Protection Engineering" (2nd Edition). Guidance is also contained in the National Fire Protection Association Fire Code 204M "Guide for Smoke and Heat Venting".

Note: Ventilation of heat and smoke may also be required for the purpose of protecting the means of escape (see Section B1) in large and complex buildings such as shopping centres (see also 3.5.3), large assembly and recreation buildings and buildings with an atrium (see 3.5.5).

Appendix A
Performance of Materials and Structures

General

A1 Many of the provisions in this Document are given in terms of performance in relation to standard methods of tests identified below. In such cases the material, product or structure should:

(a) be shown by test to be capable of meeting that performance, or

(b) have been assessed, analysed and appraised as meeting that performance (for this purpose, competent persons, laboratories accredited for conducting the relevant test, and other approving bodies might be expected to have the necessary expertise), or

(c) where tables of notional performance are included in this Document, conform with an appropriate specification given in these tables, or

(d) in the case of fire-resisting elements, conform with an appropriate specification given in Part II of the Building Research Establishments' Report (BR 128) 'Guidelines for the construction of fire-resisting structural elements' .

A2 Building Regulations deal with fire safety in buildings as a whole and they are aimed at limiting fire hazard.

The aim of standard fire tests is to measure or assess the response of a material, product, structure or system to one or more aspects of fire behaviour. Standard fire tests cannot normally measure fire hazard. They form only one of a number of factors that need to be taken into account. Other factors are those set out in this Technical Guidance Document.

Fire Resistance

A3 Factors having a bearing on fire resistance, that are considered in this document, are:

(a) fire severity,

(b) building height, or depth,

(c) building occupancy, and

(d) intervention by fire fighters.

A4 The standards of fire resistance given are based on assumptions about the severity of fires and the consequences should an element fail. Fire severity is estimated in very broad terms from the use of the building (its purpose group), on the assumption that the building contents (which constitute the fire load) are the same for buildings in the same use. In the simplest terms, the concentration of combustible material indicates the maximum temperature to which construction elements may be heated.

From estimates of the amount of combustible material per unit of floor area in various types of building (the fire load density), which were made for the Post-War Building Study No. 20 on the Fire Grading of Buildings, minimum standards have been devised for fire resistance. In this Technical Guidance Document, these basic standards have been modified according to particular features of the building affecting the risk to life, which are:

(a) height of the top floor above ground, which affects the ease of escape and of fire fighting operations, and the consequences should large scale collapse occur;

(b) occupancy, which reflects the ease with which the building can be evacuated quickly;

(c) basements, where the lack of an external wall through which to vent heat and smoke may increase heat build-up as well as complicating fire-fighting, thereby prolonging the fire; and

(d) single storey construction, where escape is direct and structural failure is unlikely to precede evacuation.

Because the use of buildings is subject to change, a precise estimate of fire severity based on the fire load due to a particular use may be misleading. A fire engineering approach of this kind must show a suitable factor of safety, to cater for these possible variations in fire load.

Fire Resistance Performance

A5 Performance in terms of the fire resistance to be met by elements of structure, doors and other forms of construction is determined by reference to BS 476: Parts 20-24: 1987 (or to BS 476: Part 8: 1972 in respect of items tested or assessed prior to 1 January 1988) in respect of one or more of the following criteria:

(a) resistance to collapse (loadbearing capacity), which applies to loadbearing elements;

(b) resistance to fire, smoke and hot gases penetration (integrity), which applies to fire separating elements; and

(c) resistance to the transfer of excessive heat (insulation), which applies to fire separating elements.

Table A1 gives the specific requirements for each element in terms of the three performance criteria above (provisions for fire doors are set out in Appendix B, Table B1).

Table A2 sets out the minimum periods of fire resistance for elements of structure.

Table A3 sets out criteria appropriate to the suspended ceilings that can be accepted as contributing to the fire resistance of a floor.

Table A4 sets out limitations on the use of uninsulated fire-resisting glazed elements.

Results of tests on fire-resisting elements are given in the following publications:

Association of Specialist Fire Protection Contractors and Manufacturers (ASFPCM)

- Fire protection for structural steel in buildings, 1992 (available from the ASFPCM, Association House, 235 Ash Road, Aldershot, Hampshire GU 12 4DD, England.

Loss Prevention Council (LPC)

- Rules for the construction and installation of firebreak doors and shutters, 1988. (available from the LPC, Melrose Avenue, Borehamwood, Herts, WD6 2BJ, England).

Information on tested elements is also frequently given in literature available from manufacturers and trade associations. Any reference used to substantiate the fire resistance rating of a construction should be carefully checked to ensure that it is suitable, adequate and applicable to the construction to be used. Small differences in detail (such as fixing method, joints, dimensions, etc.) may significantly affect the rating.

Fire resisting elements of construction should be strictly in accordance with the specification and method of construction which, by the criteria indicated at A1, can be shown to be capable of meeting the required performance. Fire resisting elements of construction should not incorporate any components, such as building services, which could compromise their fire resistance performance. Any openings for services which pass through fire resisting construction should be adequately protected and fire stopped to ensure that the fire resistance of the element is not impaired (see 3.4). Care and attention of detail should also be taken at the junctions between fire resisting elements of construction to ensure that the integrity of the fire resistance is maintained.

Roofs

A6 Performance in terms of the resistance of roofs to external fire exposure is determined by reference to the methods specified in BS 476: Part 3: 1958 under which constructions are designated by 2 letters in the range A to D, with an AA designation being the best. The first letter indicates the time to penetration, and the second letter a measure of the spread of flame. Note that this is not the most recent version of the standard.

In some circumstances, a roof or part of a roof may require a fire resistance rating, for example if it is used as part of an escape route (see B1). See also B3 and A5 for performance in terms of fire resistance.

Table A5 gives notional designations of some generic roof coverings.

Internal Linings

A7 Flame spread over wall or ceiling surfaces is controlled by providing for the lining materials or products to meet given performance levels in tests appropriate to the materials or products involved.

A8 Lining systems which can be effectively tested for 'surface spread of flame' are rated for performance by reference to the method specified in BS 476: Part 7: 1971 or 1987 under which materials or products are classified 1, 2, 3, or 4 - with Class 1 being the highest (Class 4 ratings are not acceptable under the provisions in this document).

A9 To restrict to a minimum the use of materials which ignite easily, have a high rate of heat release and/or which reduce the time to flashover, maximum acceptable 'fire propagation' indices are specified. These are determined by reference to the method specified in BS 476: Part 6: 1981 or 1989. Index of performance (I) relates to the overall test performance, whereas sub-index (i_1) is derived from the first three minutes of test.

A10 The highest product performance classification is Class 0. This is achieved if a material or the surface together with its substrate of a composite product is either:

(a) composed throughout of materials of limited combustibility (see A16), or

(b) a Class 1 material which has a fire propagation index (I) of not more than 12 and sub-index (i_1) of not more than 6.

Note: Class 0 is not a classification identified in any Standard test.

A11 Composite products defined as materials of limited combustibility (see A16) in Table A7 should in addition comply with the test requirement appropriate to any surface rating specified in Sections B2, B3 and B4.

A12 No thermoplastic material in isolation can be assumed to protect a surface underlying it. The surface rating of both products must meet the required classification. If however, the thermoplastic material is fully bonded to a non-thermoplastic substrate, then only the surface rating of the composite will need to comply.

A13 The notional performance ratings of certain widely-used generic materials or products are listed in Table A6 in terms of their performance in the traditional lining tests (BS 476: Parts 6 and 7).

Note: Information on tests on proprietary materials is frequently given in literature available from manufacturers and trade associations.

Any reference used to substantiate the surface spread of flame rating of a material or product should be carefully checked to ensure that it is suitable, adequate and applicable to the construction to be used. Small differences in detail, such as thickness, substrate, fixings, adhesive etc., may significantly affect the rating.

A14 A thermoplastic material means any polymeric material which has a softening point below 200°C if tested to BS 2782: Part 1: Method 120A: 1990. Specimens for this test may be fabricated from the original polymer where the thickness of material of the end product is less than 2.5mm.

For the purposes of Sections B2 and B4 thermoplastic materials should be used according to the performance set out in A8 and A9 above or be classified as TP(a) or TP(b) as follows:

TP(a) rigid:

(i) Rigid solid pvc sheet;

(ii) solid (as distinct from double- or multiple-skin) polycarbonate sheet at least 3mm thick;

(iii) multi-skinned rigid sheet made from unplasticised pvc or polycarbonate which has Class 1 rating when tested to BS 476: Part 7: 1971 or 1987;

(iv) any other rigid thermoplastic product, a specimen of which, when tested to BS 2782: 1970 as amended in 1974: method 508A, performs so that the test flame extinguishes before the first mark, and the duration of flaming or afterglow does not exceed 5 seconds following removal of the burner.

TP(b):

(i) Rigid solid polycarbonate sheet products less than 3 mm thick, or multiple skin polycarbonate sheet products which do not qualify as TP(a) by test; or

(ii) Other products which, when a specimen of the material between 1.5 and 3 mm thick is tested in accordance with BS 2782: 1970, as amended in 1974: method 508A, has a rate of burning which does not exceed 50 mm/minute (if it is not possible to cut or machine a 3 mm thick specimen from the product then a 3 mm test specimen can be moulded from the same material as that used for the manufacture of the product); and

(iii) the product, when ignited, does not produce burning droplets which could contribute to the spread of fire within a building.

A15 Concessions are made for thermoplastic materials used for windows, rooflights and within suspended ceilings if they cannot be tested as specified in pars. A8 and A9. They are described in Sections B2 and B4.

Materials of Limited Combustibility

A16 Materials of limited combustibility are defined in Table A7 by reference to the method specified in BS 476: Part 11: 1982. Table A7 also includes composite products (such as plasterboard) which are considered acceptable, and where they are exposed as linings they should also meet any appropriate flame spread rating.

Non-combustible Materials

A17 Non-combustible materials are defined in Table A8 either as listed products, or in terms of performance when tested to BS 476: Part 4: 1970 or Part 11: 1982.

Only these materials may be used where there is a provision for non-combustibility and also for the specific application in the elements listed in Table A8. Non-combustible materials may be used whenever there is a requirement for materials of limited combustibility.

Fire Test Methods

A18 A guide to the various test methods in BS 476 and BS 2782 is given in PD 6520: 1988 (BSI)

A guide to the development and presentation of fire tests and their use in hazard assessment is given in BS 6336: 1982.

Structural Fire Design

A19 Guidance on the design of fire-resisting structural elements for different structural materials is contained in Part 1 of the Building Research Establishment Report (BR 128) "Guidelines for the construction of fire-resisting structural elements".

Guidance on the performance of fire-resisting masonry elements is contained in I.S. 325: Part 2: 1995. Code of practice for the use of masonry, Part 2 Masonry construction.

Attention is drawn to the fire parts of the Structural Eurocodes, which have been issued by CEN (European Committee for Standardisation), as provisional Euronorms and may only be used where applicable, subject to the limitations and other modifications contained in the relevant national application document available from the National Standards Authority of Ireland.

Table A1 **Specific provisions of test for fire resistance of elements of structure, etc.**				
Part of building	**Minimum provisions when tested to relevant parts of BS 476 (1) (minutes)**			**Method of exposure**
	Loadbearing capacity (2)	**Integrity**	**Insulation**	
1. Structural frame, beam or column	*	No provision	No provision	Exposed faces
2. Loadbearing wall (which is not also a wall described in any of the following items)	*	No provision	No provision	each side separately
3. Floors				
(a) floor in upper storey of a 2 storey house (but not over a garage)	30	15	15	from underside (3)
(b) any other floor including compartment floors	*	*	*	from underside (3)
4. Roofs Any part forming an escape route	30	30	30	from underside (3)
5. External walls				
(a) any part less than 1m from any point on relevant boundary	*	*	*	each side separately
(b) any part 1m or more from the relevant boundary	*	*	15(4)	from inside
6. Separating wall (5)	* (min 60)	* (min 60)	* (min 60)	each side separately
7. Compartment wall	*	*	*	each side separately
8. Protected shafts excluding any firefighting shaft				
(a) any glazing described in Section B3, 3.2.7.3 and Diagram 15	N/A	30	No provision(6)	each side separately
(b) any other part between the shaft and a protected lobby/corridor described in Diagram 15	30	30	30	each side separately
(c) any part not described in (a) or (b) above	*	*	*	each side separately
9. Enclosure (which does not form part of a compartment wall or a protected shaft) to a -				
(a) protected stairway	30	30	30(6)	each
(b) lift shaft, or	30	30	30	side
(c) service shaft,	30	30	30	separately
10. Firefighting shafts:				
(a) construction separating firefighting shaft from rest of building	120 60	120 60	120 60	from side remote from shaft from shaft side
(b) construction separating firefighting stairway, firefighting lift shaft and firefighting lobby	60	60	60	each side separately

Table A1 (contd) **Specific provisions of test for fire resistance of elements of structure, etc.**				
Part of building	**Minimum provisions when tested to relevant parts of BS 476 (1) (minutes)**			**Method of exposure**
	Loadbearing capacity (2)	**Integrity**	**Insulation**	
11. Enclosure (which is not a compartment wall or described in item 8) to a - (a) protected lobby, or (b) protected corridor	 30 30	 30 30	 30(6) 30	each side separately
12. Subdivision of a corridor	30	30	30(6)	each side separately
13. Wall separating an attached or integral garage from a dwelling house	30	30	30	from garage side
14. Enclosure to a - (a) protected entrance, hall, or (b) protected stairway in a flat or maisonette	 30 30	 30 30	 30(6) 30(6)	each side separately
15. Fire-resisting construction in dwellings not described elsewhere	30	30	30(6)	each side separately
16. Cavity barrier	No provision	30	15	each side separately
17. Ceiling described in Diagrams 18 and 19	N/A	30	30	from underside
18. Duct described in Section B3, paragraph 3.3.5(e)	N/A	30	No provision	from outside
19. Casing around a drainage system described in 3.4 and Diagram 22	N/A	30	No provision	from outside
20. Flue walls described in 3.4.4 and Diagrams 24	N/A	*	*	from outside
21. Fire doors	See Table B1 of Appendix B			

Notes

* Denotes minimum period of fire resistance set out in Table A2.

N/A Denotes that provision is not applicable.

(1) BS 476 Part 21 for loadbearing elements, Part 22 for non-loadbearing elements, Part 23 for fire-protecting suspended ceilings; and Part 24 for ventilation ducts (tests to BS 476: Part 8 are permitted subject to paragraph A5).

(2) Applies to loadbearing elements only.

(3) A suspended ceiling should only be relied on to contribute to the fire resistance of the floor if the ceiling meets the appropriate provisions given in Table A3.

(4) 30 mins for any part adjacent to an external escape route (but no provision for glazed elements in respect of insulation).

(5) See Part B3, 3.2.5.6 for requirements for construction of separating walls.

(6) Except for any limitations on glazed elements given in Table A4.

Table A2	Minimum periods of fire resistance for elements of structure					
Purpose group of buildings	**Minimum period (minutes) for elements of structure in a -**					
	Basement storey # (including floor over)		**Ground or upper storey**			
	Depth (3) (m) of lowest basement		**Height (3) (m) of top storey in building or of separated part**			
	more than 10	not more than 10	not more than 5	not more than 20	not more than 30	more than 30
1. Residential (Domestic)						
- Houses	-	30*	30*	30*	-	-
- Flats and maisonettes	90	60	30*	60**	90**	120**
2. Residential						
(a) Institutional	90	60	60	60	90	120ø
(b) Other residential	90	60	30*	60	90	120ø
3. Office						
- not sprinklered	90	60	30*	60	90	x
- sprinklered	60	60	30*	30*	60	120ø
4 (a) Shop						
- not sprinklered	90	60	60	60	90	x
- sprinklered (1)	60	60	30*	60	60	120ø
4 (b) Shopping Centre	See 3.5.3		See 3.5.3			
5. Assembly and Recreation						
- not sprinklered	90	60	60	60	90	x
- sprinklered (1)	60	60	30*	60	60	120ø
6. Industrial						
- not sprinklered	120	90	60	90	120	x
- sprinklered (1)	90	60	30*	60	90	120ø
7(b) Car park						
(i) open sided (2)	x	x	15*	15*	15*	x
(ii) any other	90	60	30*	60	90	120ø
7(a) Storage and 8. Other non-residential						
- not sprinklered	120	90	60	90	120	x
- sprinklered	90	60	30*	60	90	120ø

Notes

x not permitted

Modifications

* Increased to 60 minutes for separating walls

** Reduced to 30 minutes for any floor within a maisonette (but not if the floor contributes to the support of the building as a whole)

ø Reduced to 90 minutes for elements not forming part of the structural frame

≠ The floor over a basement (or if there is more than 1 basement, the floor over the topmost basement) should meet the provisions for the ground and upper storeys if that period is higher.

(1) "Sprinklered" means that the building is fitted throughout with an automatic sprinkler system meeting the relevant recommendations of BS 5306: Part 2, i.e. the relevant occupancy rating together with the additional requirements for life safety.

(2) The car park should comply with the relevant provisions in Section B3, 3.5.2. Refer to Table A1 for specific provisions of test.

(3) For height of top storey or depth of basement, see Appendix C, Diagram 38.

Refer to Table A1 for specific provisions of test for fire resistance of elements of structure.

Application of the Fire Resistance Standards in Table A2

(a) Where one element of structure supports or carries or gives stability to another, the fire resistance of the supporting element should be no less than the minimum period of fire resistance for the other element (whether that other element is loadbearing or not).

There are circumstances where it may be reasonable to vary this principle, for example where the supporting structure is in the open air; or

(b) Where an element of structure forms part of more than one building or compartment, that element should be constructed to the standard of the greater of the relevant provisions.

(c) Although some elements of structure in a single storey building may be excluded from needing fire resistance (see B3, par. 3.1.4(a)), fire resistance will be needed if the element:

(i) is part of (or supports) an external wall and there is provision in B4 to limit the extent of openings and other unprotected areas in the wall; or

(ii) is part of (or supports) a compartment wall, a separating wall or a wall between a dwelling house and an attached or integral garage; or

(iii) supports a gallery.

For the purposes of this paragraph, the ground storey of a building which has one or more basement storeys and no upper storeys, may be considered as single storey. The fire resistance of the basement storeys should be that appropriate to basements.

(d) Where one side of a basement is (due to the slope of the ground) open at ground level, giving an opportunity for smoke venting and access for fire fighting, it may be appropriate to adopt for elements of structure in that storey, the standard of fire resistance applicable to above ground structure.

Table A3 **Limitations on fire-protecting suspended ceilings**

<table>
<tr><th>Height of building or of separated part (m)</th><th>Type of floor</th><th>Provisions of fire resistance of floor (mins)</th><th>Description of suspended ceiling</th></tr>
<tr><td rowspan="3">Less than 15</td><td>not compartment</td><td>60 or less</td><td rowspan="2">Type A, B, C, or D</td></tr>
<tr><td rowspan="2">compartment</td><td>less than 60</td></tr>
<tr><td>60</td><td>Type B, C or D</td></tr>
<tr><td>15 or more</td><td>any</td><td>60 or less</td><td>Type C or D</td></tr>
<tr><td>no limit</td><td>any</td><td>more than 60</td><td>Type D</td></tr>
</table>

Notes:

Ceiling Type		Description
A	-	Surface of ceiling exposed to the cavity should be Class O or Class 1.
B	-	Surface of ceiling exposed to the cavity should be Class O.
C	-	Surface of ceiling exposed to the cavity should be Class O. Ceiling should not contain easily openable access panels.
D	-	Ceiling should be of a material of limited combustibility and not contain easily openable access panels. Any insulation above the ceiling should be of a material of limited combustibility.

Any removable panels provided in fire protecting suspended ceilings of type C or D should be secured in position by releasing devices or screw fixings, and they should be shown to be of types which have been tested in the type of ceiling assembly in which they are incorporated.

Table A4	**Limitations on the use of uninsulated fire resisting glazed elements on escape routes**			
Position of glazed element	**Maximum total glazed area in parts of a building with access to:**			
	a single stairway		**more than one stairway**	
	Walls	**Door Leaf**	**Walls**	**Door Leaf**
(1) Dwelling house (a) within the enclosures to a protected stairway or within fire-resisting construction shown in Diagram 9	Fixed fanlights only	Unlimited	Fixed fanlights only	Unlimited
(2) Within the enclosures to a protected entrance hall or protected landing of a flat or maisonette	Fixed fanlights only	Unlimited above 1.1 m	Fixed fanlights only	Unlimited above 1.1m
(3) Between residential/ sleeping accommodation and a common escape route (corridor, lobby or stairway)	Nil	Nil	Nil	Nil
(4) *Between a protected stairway (+) and - (a) the accommodation, or (b) a corridor which is not a protected corridor	Nil	25% of door area	Unlimited above 1.1 m ≠	50% of door area
(5) *Between - (a) a protected stairway (+) and a protected lobby or protected corridor: (b) the accommodation and a protected lobby	Unlimited above 1.1 m from floor	Unlimited above 0.1 m from floor	Unlimited above 1.1 m from floor	Unlimited above 0.1 m from floor
(6) *Between the accommodation and a protected corridor forming a dead end;	Unlimited above 1.1 m from floor	Unlimited above 1.1 m from floor	Unlimited above 1.1 m from floor	Unlimited above 1.1 m from floor
(7) *(a) Between the accommodation and any other corridor: (b) Subdividing corridors	N/A	N/A	Unlimited above 0.1 m from floor	Unlimited above 0.1 m from floor

Notes:

* But not any such part included in item 3.

(+) If the protected stairway is also a protected shaft (see B3) or a firefighting stairway (see B5), the use of glazed elements may be further restricted.

≠ Measured vertically from the landing floor level or the stairway pitch line.

Table A5	**Notional designations of roof coverings**	
Part 1: Pitched roofs covered with slates or tiles		
Covering Material	**Supporting Structure**	**Designation**
1. Natural slates 2. Fibre-cement slates 3. Clay tiles 4. Concrete tiles	1. Timber rafters with or without underfelt, sarking, boarding, wood wool slabs, plywood, wood chipboard, or fibre insulating board	AA
5. Strip slates of bitumen felt Class 1 or 2	2. Timber rafters and boarding, plywood, wood wool slabs, compressed straw slabs, wood chipboard, or fibre insulating board	CC
6. Bitumen felt strip slates Type 2E, with underlay of bitumen felt Type 2B	3. Timber rafters and boarding, plywood, wood wool slabs, compressed straw slabs, wood chipboard or fibre insulating board	BB

Note:

Any reference in this Table to bitumen felt of a specified type is a reference felt as so designed in I.S. 36: Part 1: 1986 and Part 2: 1987.

Table A5 **Notional designations of roof coverings**			
Part II: Pitched roofs covered with pre-formed self-supporting sheets			
Material	**Construction**	**Supporting Structure**	**Designation**
Profiled sheets of: (i) galvanised steel (ii) aluminium (iii) fibre reinforced cement (iv) pvc coated steel	1. single skin without underlay or with underlay of - (i) plasterboard (ii) fibre insulating board (iii) wood wool slab	structure of timber, steel or concrete	AA
Profiled sheets of: (i) galvanised steel (ii) aluminium (iii) composite steel and fibre-cement (iv) fibre-cement or (v) pvc coated steel	2. double skin without underlay or with underlay of - (i) resin-bonded glass fibre (ii) bitumen-bonded glass fibre (iii) mineral wool slab or blanket (iv) polystyrene or (v) polyurethane	structure of timber, steel or concrete	AA

Table A5 **Notional designations of roof coverings**		
Part III: Pitched or flat roofs covered with fully supporting material		
Covering Material	**Supporting Structure**	**Designation**
1. Aluminium sheet 2. Copper sheet 3. Zinc sheet 4. Lead sheet 5. Mastic asphalt 6. Vitreous enamelled steel sheet	1. Timber joists and - (i) tongued and grooved boarding, or (ii) plain edged boarding	AA*
	2. Steel or timber joists with deck of - (i) wood wool slab (ii) compressed straw slab (iii) wood or flax chipboard (iv) fibre insulating board, or (v) 9.5 mm plywood	AA
	3. Concrete or clay pot slab (cast in situ or precast), or non-combustible deck of steel, aluminium or fibre-cement (with or without insulation)	AA

Notes:

* Lead sheet supported by timber joints and plain edged boarding is deemed to be of designated BA.

Table A5 Notional designations of roof coverings

Part IV(A): Flat roofs covered with bitumen felt

A flat roof comprising a covering of bitumen felt shall (irrespective of the felt specification) be deemed to be of designation AA if the felt is laid on a deck constructed of any of the materials prescribed in the Table in Part IV(B) and has a surface finish of:

(a) bitumen bedded stone chippings covering the whole surface to a depth of not less than 12.5 mm

(b) bitumen bedded tiles of a non-combustible material

(c) sand and cement screed or

(d) macadam

Table A5 Notional designations of roof coverings

Part IV(B): Pitched roofs covered with bitumen felt

Number of layers	Type of upper layer	Type of under-layer(s)	Deck of either of the following (having minimum thickness stated) plywood (6mm). wood chipboard (12.5mm). T&G boarding (16mm finished) or Plain edged boarding (19mm finished)	Deck of compressed straw slab	Deck of screeded woodwool slab	Fibre-cement or steel single or double skin deck (without overlay or with overlay of fibre insulating board)	Aluminium single or double skin deck without overlay or with overlay of fibre insulating board)	Concrete or pot slab (cast in situ or precast)
Two or three layers built up in accordance with CP144: Part 3. 1970	1. Type 1E	Type 1B (minimum mass 13kg/10m²)	CC	AC	AC	AC	AC	AB
	2. Type 2E	Type 1B (minimum mass 13kg/10m²)	BB	AB	AB	AB	AB	AB
	3. Type 3E	Type 3B or 3G	BC	AC	AB	AB	AB	AB

Note:
Any reference in this Table to bitumen felt of a specified type is a reference to bitumen felt as so designated in I.S. 36: Part 1: 1986 and Part 2: 1987.

Table A6 **Typical performance ratings of some generic materials and products**

Rating	Material or Product
Class 0	1. Any non-combustible material or material of limited combustibility (composite products listed in Table A7 must meet the test requirements given in paragraph A10(b)).
	2. Brickwork, blockwork, concrete and ceramic tiles.
	3. Plasterboard (painted or not, with or without an air gap or fibrous or cellular insulating material behind.
	4. Woodwool cement slabs
	5. Mineral fibre tiles or sheets with cement or resin binding.
	6. Timber or plywood with density more than 400 kg/m^3, painted or unpainted.
Class 3	7. Wood particle board or hardboard, either treated or painted.
	8. Standard glass reinforced polyesters.

Notes:

1. Materials and products listed under Class 0 also meet Class 1.

2. The following materials and products may achieve the ratings listed below. However, as the properties of different products with the same generic description vary, the ratings of these materials/products should be substantiated by test evidence. Materials/products should also be assessed by reference to the toxic hazard they pose in combustion.

   Class 0 - aluminium faced fibre insulating board, flame retardant decorative laminates on a calcium silicate board, thick polycarbonate sheet, phenolic sheet and uPVC;

   Class 1 - phenolic or melamine laminates on a calcium silicate substrate and flame retardant decorate laminates on a combustible substrate.

Table A7 **Use of materials of limited combustibility**	
Use	**Material**
1. stairways where there is provision in Part B1, paragraph 1.4.4.1 for them to be constructed of materials of limited combustibility 2. materials above a suspended ceiling meeting the provisions in Section B3, (2)(f) of 3.3.3 3. reinforcement/support for fire-stopping referred to in Section B3, 3.4.5 4. construction in shopping complexes referred to in Section B3, 3.5.3(b) 5. roof covering meeting the provisions: (a) in Section B3, 3.3.3 or (b) in Section B4, Diagram 29 6. class 0 materials meeting the provision in Appendix A, paragraph A10(a) 7. ceiling tiles or panels of any fire-protecting suspended ceiling (Type D) in Table A3	(a), (b) or (c) below
8. Insulation above any fire-protecting suspended ceiling (Type D) in Table A3	(a), (b), (c) or (d) below

Materials of limited combustibility:

(a) Any non-combustible material listed in Table A8.

(b) Any material of density 300 kg/m^3 or more which when tested to BS 476: Part 11, does not flame and the rise in temperature on the furnace thermocouple is not more than 20 degrees celsius.

(c) Any material with a non-combustible core at least 8mm thick having combustible facings (on one or both sides) not more than 0.5 mm thick (when a flame spread rating is specified, these materials must also meet the appropriate test requirements).

(d) Any material of density less than 300 kg/m^3, which when tested to BS 476: Part 11 does not flame for more than 10 seconds and the rise in temperature on the centre (specimen) thermocouple is not more than 35 degrees celsius and on the furnace thermocouple is not more than 25 degrees celsius.

Table A8 **Use of non-combustible materials**	
Use	**Material**
1. ladders referred to in Section B1, paragraph 1.4.4.2.	any material listed below
2. roof coverings meeting the provision in Section B3, Diagram 13(a).	
3. refuse chutes meeting the provisions in Section B3, paragraph 3.2.6.2(c).	
4. suspended ceilings and their supports where provision in Section B3, 2(c) of 3.3.3 for them to be constructed of non-combustible materials.	
5. pipes meeting the provisions in Section B3, Table 3.4	
6. flue walls meeting the provisions in Section B3, Diagram 24	
7. construction forming car parks referred to in Section B3, paragraph 3.5.2.1.	
8. external surfaces of walls where there is provision in Section B4, table 4.1, for them to be constructed of non-combustible materials.	
9. hinges meeting the provisions in Appendix B, paragraph B5.	
10. compartment walls and floors required by 3.2.5 of Section B3 to be constructed of non-combustible materials.	

Non-combustible materials:

(a) Any material which when tested to BS 476: Part II: 1982 does not flame and there is no rise in temperature on either the centre (specimen) or furnace thermocouples.

(b) Totally inorganic materials such as concrete, fired clay, ceramics, metals, plaster and masonry containing not more than 1 per cent by weight or volume of organic material (use in buildings of combustible metals such as magnesium/aluminium alloys should be assessed in each individual case).

(c) Concrete bricks or blocks meeting I.S. 20: 1974; I.S. 20, Part 1: 1987 or I.S. 189: 1974.

(d) Products classified as non-combustible under BS 476: Part 4: 1970.

Appendix B
Fire Doors

General

B1 A fire door is a door or shutter, provided for the passage of persons, air or objects, which together with its frame and furniture as installed in a building is intended when closed to resist the passage of fire and/or gaseous products of combustion, and is capable of meeting specified performance criteria to those ends (see definition of a fire door in Appendix D).

Any reference to a fire door in this Technical Guidance Document, or in any code of practice or other document referred to in this technical guidance document, is intended to mean a complete door assembly which includes the door leaf or leaves, the door frame, ironmongery (hinges, latches, closers, etc.) and any seals where required between the frame and leaf or between leaves in the case of a twin-leaf door, and which is installed in a building and is capable of meeting the required performance. The performance of a fire door critically depends on the correct installation of the complete door assembly, strictly in accordance with the terms of the relevant test certification supplied by the door manufacturer.

All fire doors should have the appropriate performance given in Table B1. In this table, doors are identified by their performance under test to BS 476: Part 22, in terms of integrity for a period of minutes, eg FD30. A suffix (S) is added for doors where restricted smoke leakage at ambient temperatures is needed. The method of test exposure is from each side of the door separately, except in the case of lift doors which are tested from the landing side only.

BS 8214: 1990 Code of Practice for fire door assemblies with non-metallic leaves, makes recommendations relating to the specification, design, manufacture, installation and maintenance of timber fire doors.

Self-closing Devices

B2 All fire doors should be fitted with an automatic self-closing device which is capable of closing the door from any angle and against any latch fitted to the door.

Note: Fire doors to cupboards and to service ducts may be normally kept locked shut in lieu of being fitted with a self-closing device.

B3 Where a self-closing device would be considered a hindrance to the normal use of the building, fire doors may be held open by:

(a) a fusible link (but not if the door is fitted in an opening provided as a means of escape unless it complies with paragraph B4 below); or

(b) an electro-magnetic or electro-mechanical device which will automatically release the door on activation of an adjacent smoke detector on the fire alarm system, if the door can also be closed manually and it is not to be -

   (i) the only escape stairway serving a building (or part of a building), or

   (ii) a firefighting stairway, or

   (iii) an escape stairway serving a building in any residential purpose group;

   or

(c) a door closure delay device.

B4 Two fire doors may be fitted in the same opening so that the total fire resistance is the sum of their individual fire resistances, provided that each door is capable of closing the opening. Where two fire doors are fitted in the same opening that is provided as a means of escape, one door may be fitted with an automatic self-closing device and be held open by a fusible link if the other door is capable of being easily opened by hand and has at least 30 minutes fire resistance.

Fire Door Hardware

B5 Any hinge on which a fire door is hung should be made entirely from non-combustible materials having a melting point of at least 800°C. Hardware used on fire doors can significantly affect performance in fire. Guidance is available in a "Code of practice for hardware essential to the optimum performance of fire resisting timber doorsets" published by the Association of Builders' Hardware Manufacturers in 1983.

Fire Safety Signs

B6 The following applies to the provision of fire safety signs on fire doors:

(a) Except for doors identified in (b) below, all fire doors should be marked (at about eye level) with the appropriate fire safety sign complying with BS 5499: Part 1: 1990 (mandatory signs as set out in Appendix A and Appendix B of that document) according to whether the door is:

(i) to be kept closed when not in use,

(ii) to be kept locked when not in use, or

(iii) held open by an electro-magnetic or electro-mechanical device.

Fire doors to cupboards and to service ducts should be marked on the outside; all other fire doors on both sides.

(b) The following fire doors are not required to comply with (a) above;

(i) doors within dwelling houses,

(ii) doors to and within flats or maisonettes,

(iii) bedroom doors in Other Residential (Purpose Group 2(b) premises, and

(iv) lift entrance doors.

Identification

B7 All fire doors installed in a building should be permanently identified in accordance with the recommendations of BS 8214: 1990, to indicate the period of fire resistance, the manufacturer, year of manufacture, and other pertinent details. Every fire door (i.e. the complete fire door assembly) should be supported by a fire test report and assessment from an accredited laboratory (see Technical Guidance Document D), which indicates that the complete assembly will meet the required performance (see B1 above).

Performance

B8 Tables A1 and A2 of Appendix A sets out the minimum periods of fire resistance for elements of structure to which the performance of some doors is linked. Table A4 sets out limitations on the use of uninsulated fire resisting glazed elements on escape routes.

Table B1 **Provisions for fire doors**	
Position of door	**Minimum fire resistance in terms of integrity (minutes) See notes(1 to 4)**
1. Within a separating wall	FD *S (min. 60)
2. Within a compartment wall -	
(a) if it separates a flat or maisonette from a space in common use,	FD 30S
(b) enclosing a protected shaft forming a stairway situated wholly or partly above the adjoining ground in a building used for flats, other residential, assembly and recreation or office purposes,	FD 30S
(c) enclosing a protected shaft forming a stairway not described in (b) above,	FD + S (min. 30)
(d) not described in (a), (b) or (c) above	FD* (see Note 5)
3. Within a compartment floor	FD *S
4. Forming part of the enclosures (which does not form a protected shaft) of a -	
(a) protected stairway (except where described in item 9 below);	FD 30S
(b) lift shaft, or	FD 30
(c) service shaft,	FD 30S
5. Forming part of the enclosure of a -	
(a) a protected lobby approach (or corridor) to a stairway,	FD 30S
(b) any other protected corridor,	FD 30S
6. Affording access to an external escape route	FD 30
7. Sub-dividing -	
(a) corridors connecting alternative exits,	FD 30S
(b) dead-end portions of corridors from the remainder of the corridor	FD 30S
8. Any door -	
(a) within a cavity barrier,	FD 20
(b) between a dwelling house and a garage	FD 30
9. Any door -	
(a) forming part of the enclosures to a protected stairway in a dwelling house,	FD 20
(b) forming part of the enclosures to a protected entrance hall or protected landing in a flat or maisonette	FD 20
(c) within any other fire-resisting construction in a dwelling not described elsewhere	FD 20

Notes:

* Period of fire resistance (see Table A1 of Appendix A) for the wall in which the door is situated.

\+ Half the period of fire resistance (see Table A1 of Appendix A) for the wall in which the door is situated, but not less than 30 minutes.

S Unless pressurization techniques complying with BS 5588: Part 4: 1979 are used, these doors should also have leakage rate not exceeding 3 m^3/m/hour (head and jambs only) when tested at 25 Pa under BS 476: Section 31.1.

(1) To BS 476: Part 22: 1987 (or BS 476: Part 8 subject to paragraph A5 of Appendix A).
(2) Method of exposure is from each side separately (except for doors to lift shafts, which is from the landing side only).
(3) Two fire-resisting doors may be fitted in an opening if each door by itself is capable of closing the opening and the two doors together achieve the required level of fire resistance.
(4) See also Appendix A, Table A4, for limitation on use of uninsulated glazed elements.
(5) FD*S if the door is in a compartment wall used for horizontal evacuation in a hospital (see B1, 1.2.7).

Appendix C
Methods of Measurement

Methods of Measurement

C1 Some form of measurement is an integral part of many of the provisions in this Document. Diagrams 34 to 38 show how the various forms of measurement should be made, based on definitions in Appendix D.

Note: See Section B1, par. 1.0.10 for methods of measurement specific to means of escape in case of fire.

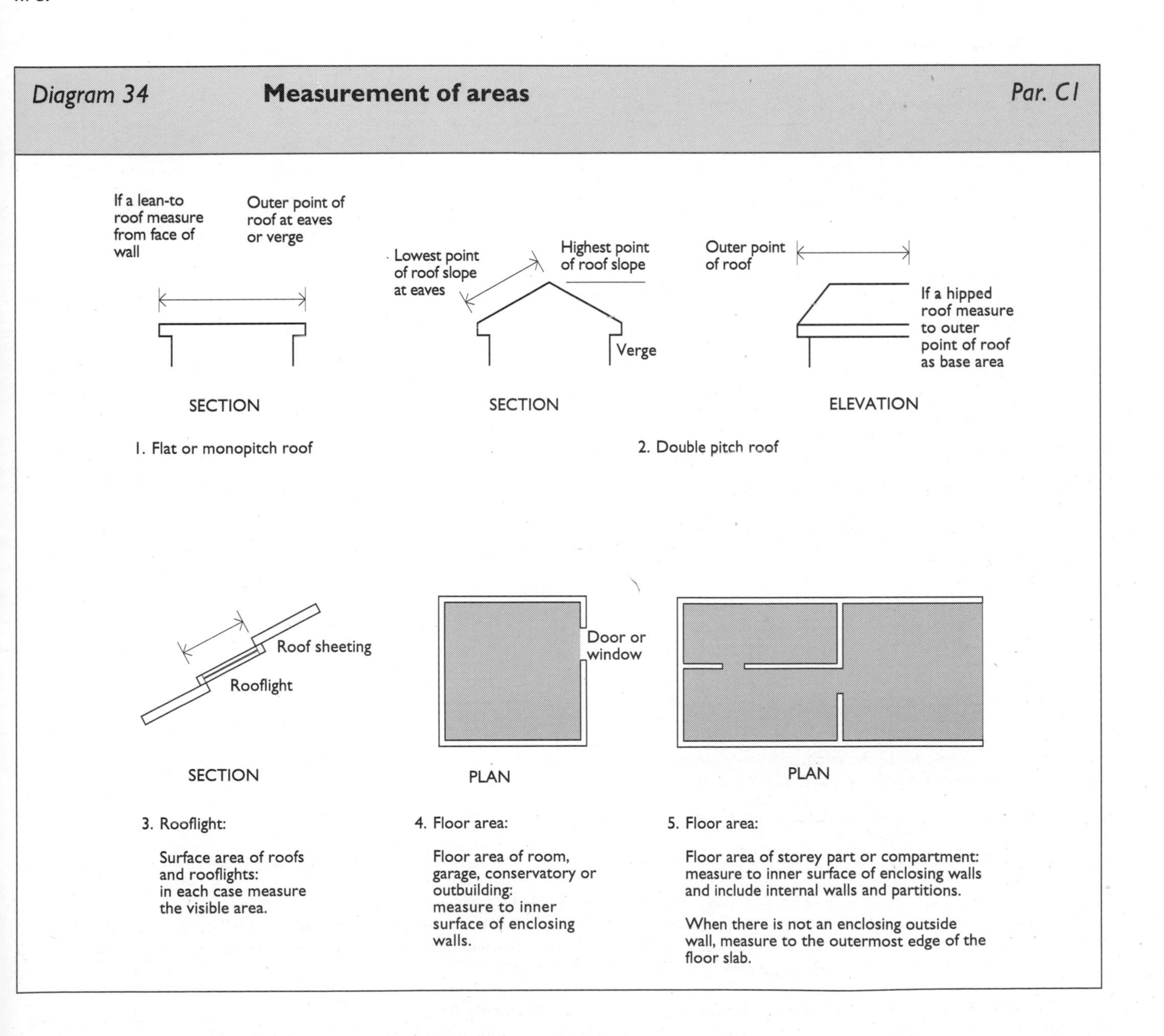

Diagram 34 **Measurement of areas** *Par. C1*

Diagram 35 **Cubic capacity** *Par. C1*

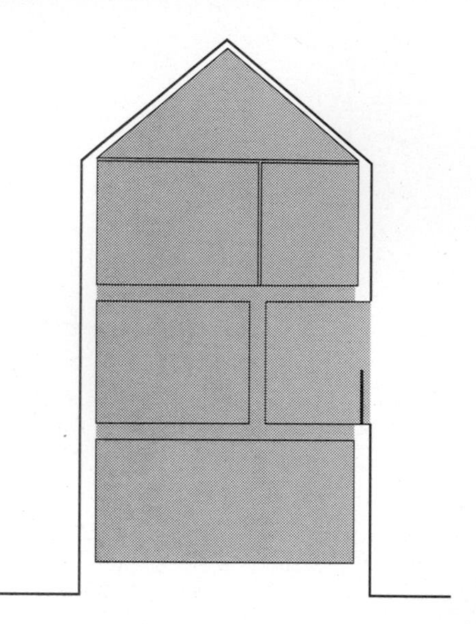

1. CUBIC CAPACITY OF BUILDING

Measure

- to upper side of lowest floor
- to lower side of roof
- to inner surface of enclosing walls or, where there is not an enclosing outside wall, to the outermost edge of the floor

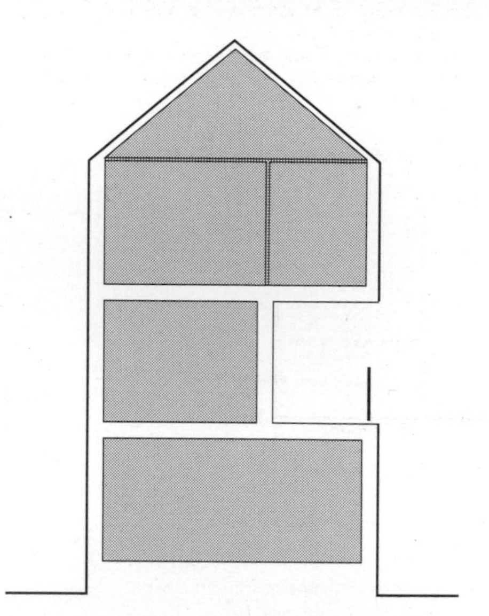

2. CUBIC CAPACITY OF A COMPARTMENT

Measure

- to lower side of compartment floor over
- to upper side of compartment floor below
- to inner surface of compartment walls

KEY

Partition

Compartment wall or floor

Diagram 36 **Number of storeys** *Par. C1*

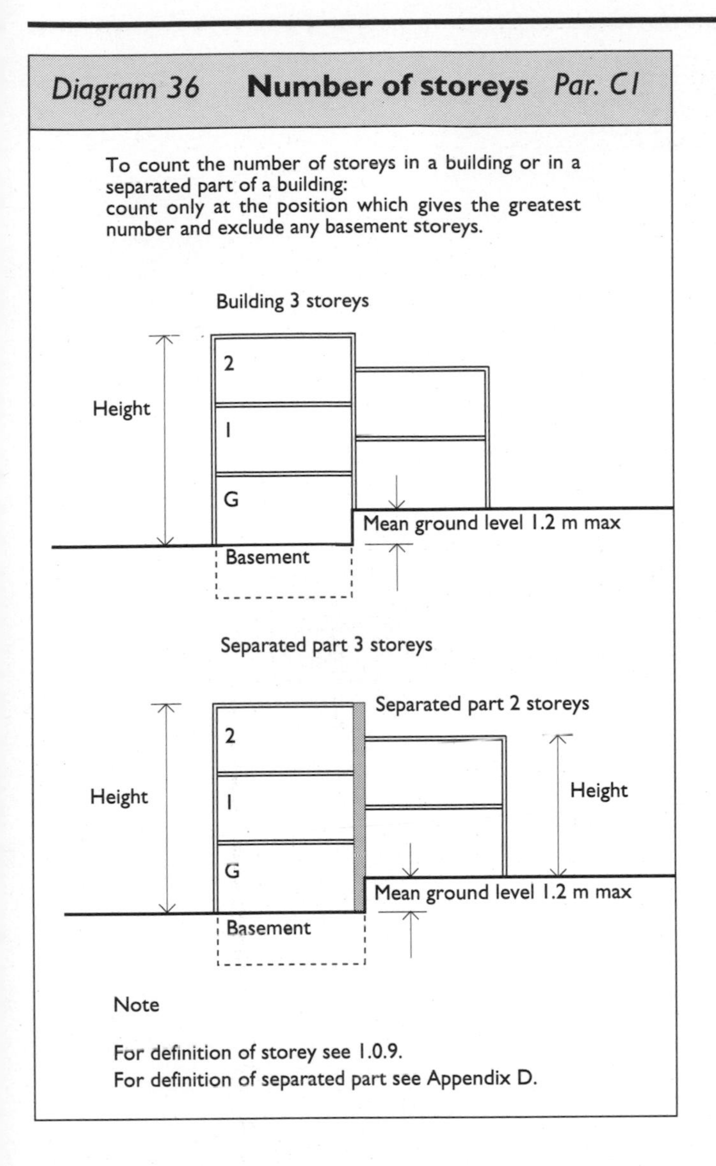

Diagram 37 Height of a building Par. C1

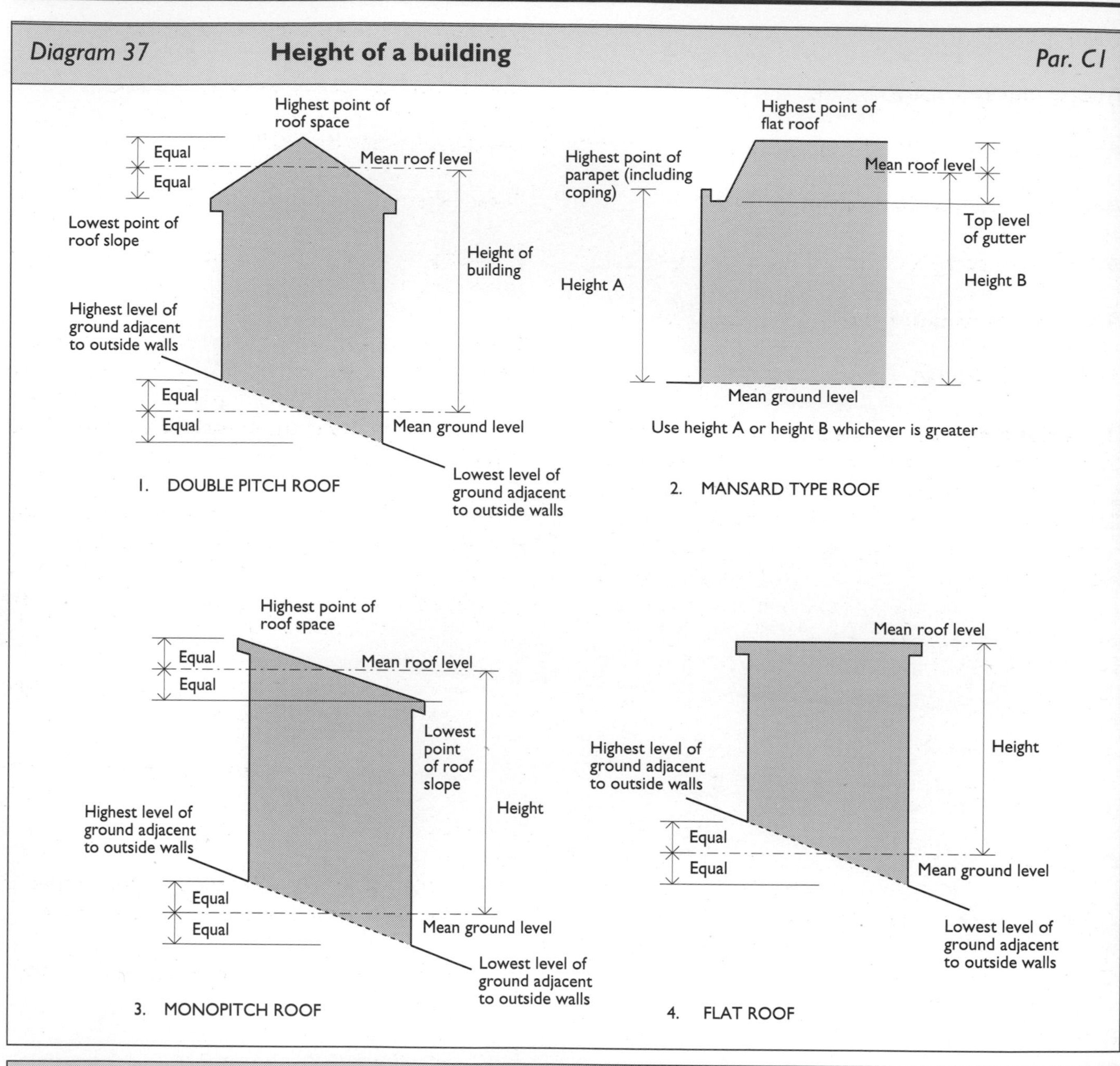

Diagram 38 Height of top storey and depth of a basement Par. C1

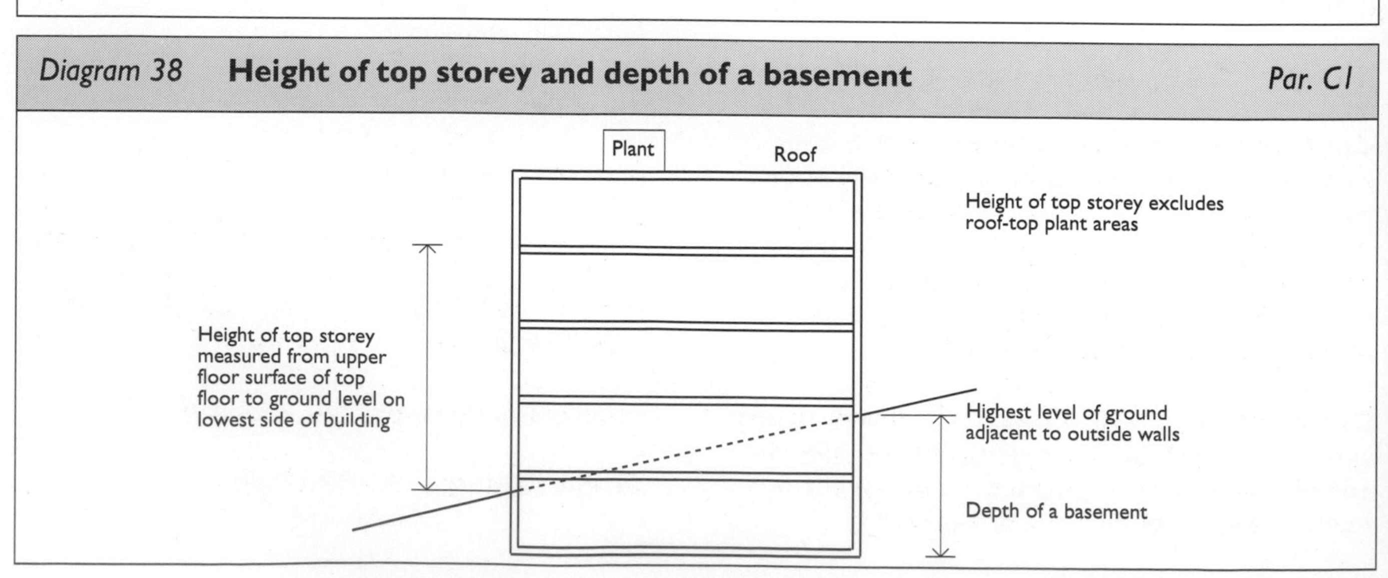

Appendix D
Definitions

Definitions

Access room - See B1 (1.0.9)

Access level - See B1 (1.0.9)

Accommodation stairway - See B1 (1.0.9)

Alternative escape routes - See B1(1.0.9)

Appliance ventilation duct - See B3 (3.0.5)

Atrium (plural atria) - See B1 (1.0.9)

Basement storey - means a storey which is below the ground storey or, where there is no ground storey, means a storey the top surface of the floor of which is situated at such a level or levels that some point on its perimeter is more than 1.2 m below the level of the finished surface of the ground adjoining the building in the vicinity of that point (however, see Appendix A, Table A2, for concessions where the storey is considered to be a basement only because of a sloping site)

Bedroom - See B1 (1.0.9)

Boundary - See B4 (4.0.2)

Cavity - See B2 (2.0.7)

Cavity Barrier - See B3 (3.0.5)

Ceiling - See B2 (2.0.7)

Circulation space - See B2 (2.0.7)

Class O - See Appendix A, paragraph A10

Compartment (fire compartment) - A building or part of a building, comprising one or more rooms, spaces or storeys, constructed to prevent the spread of fire to or from another part of the same building, or an adjoining building (a roof space above the top storey of a compartment is included in that compartment) (see also 'Separated Part')

Compartment wall/floor - A fire-resisting wall/floor used in the separation of one fire compartment from another (constructional requirements are given in 3.2 of Section B3)

Concealed space (cavity) - See B3 (3.0.5)

Conservatory - See B4 (4.0.2)

Dead-end - See B1 (1.0.9)

Direct distance - See B1 (1.0.9)

Dwelling - A single-family dwelling house, a flat or maisonette

Electro-magnetic, or electro-mechanical device susceptible to smoke - A device which will allow a door held open by it to close automatically in the event of each or any one of the following:

(a) detection of smoke by automatic apparatus suitable in nature, quality and location, and

(b) operation of a manually operated switch fitted in a suitable position, and

(c) failure of the electricity supply to the device, apparatus or switch, and

(d) operation of the fire alarm system, if any.

Element of structure -

(a) a member forming part of the structural frame of a building or any other beam or column, and

(b) a loadbearing wall or loadbearing part of a wall, and

(c) a floor, and

(d) a gallery, and

(e) an external wall, and

(f) a compartment wall (including a separating wall).

However, see B3, par. 3.1.4, for exclusions from the provisions for elements of structure

Emergency lighting - See B1 (1.0.9)

Escape lighting - See B1 (1.0.9)

Escape route - See B1 (1.0.9)

Evacuation lift - See B1 (1.0.9)

External wall - See B4 (4.0.2)

Final exit - See B1 (1.0.9)

Fire door - A door or shutter, provided for the passage of persons, air or objects, which together with its frame and furniture as installed in a building is intended when closed to resist the passage of fire and/or gaseous products of combustion, and is capable of meeting specified performance criteria to those ends (it may have one or more leaves and includes a cover or other form of protection to an opening in a fire-resisting wall or floor, or in a structure surrounding a protected shaft)

Firefighting lift - See B5 (5.0.4)

Firefighting lobby - See B5 (5.0.4)

Firefighting shaft - See B5 (5.0.4)

Firefighting stairway - See B5 (5.0.4)

Fire mains - See B5 (5.0.5)

Fire stop - See B3 (3.0.5)

Flat - Separate and self-contained premises constructed or adopted for residential use and forming part of a building from some other part of which it is divided horizontally.

Floor area - in relation to a building means the area bounded by the inner finished surfaces of the enclosing walls, or, on any side where there is no enclosing wall, by the outermost edge of the floor on that side and in calculating the area of a building or part of a building there shall be included in such area the space occupied by any walls, shafts, ducts or structure within the area being measured (see Diagram 34 of Appendix C)

Gallery - A floor, including a raised storage area, which is less than one-half of the area of the space into which it projects

Hydrant - See B5 (5.0.4)

Habitable room - See B1 (1.0.9)

Height (of a building or storey) - (or of part of a building which is completely separated throughout, both below and above ground, by a compartment wall or compartment walls in the same continuous vertical plane) means the height of such building or part measured from the mean level of the ground adjoining the outside of the external wall of the building to the level of half the vertical height of the roof of the building or part, or to the top of the walls or of the parapet (if any), whichever is the higher (see Diagram 37 of Appendix C)

Inner room - See B1 (1.0.9)

Maisonette - A dwelling forming part of a larger building, which has its rooms divided between two or more levels which are more than half a storey height apart

Materials of limited combustibility - See Appendix A, paragraph A16 and Table A7

Means of escape - See B1 (1.0.9)

Measurement
For area, cubic capacity, height of a building and number of storeys) - See Appendix C, Diagrams 34 to 38. For occupant capacity, seatway, travel distance and width of a doorway, escape route and a stairway - See B1, paragraph 1.0.10

Non-combustible - See Appendix A, paragraph A17 and Table A8

Notional boundary - See B4 (4.0.2)

Open spatial planning - See B1 (1.0.9)

Perimeter (of Building) - See B5 (5.0.4)

Pipe (for the purposes of B3) - See B3 (3.0.5)

Place of safety - See B1 (1.0.9)

Places of special fire risk - See B1 (1.0.9)

Platform floor - See B3 (3.0.5)

Pressurization - See B1 (1.0.9)

Protected corridor/escape route lobby - See B1 (1.0.9)

Protected shaft - A shaft which enables persons, air or objects to pass from one compartment to another and is enclosed with fire-resisting construction

Protected stairway - See B1 (1.0.9)

Purpose group - See Section B0 paragraph 0.3.2, and Table 0.1

Relevant boundary - See B4 (4.0.2)

Rooflight - See B2 (2.0.7) or B4 (4.0.2)

Room - See B2 (2.0.7)

Separated part (of a building) - A form of compartmentation that is a part which is separated from another part of the same building by a compartment wall which runs full height of the part and is in one plane (see Appendix C, Diagram 36)

Separating wall - See B3 (3.0.5)

Single storey building - A building consisting of a ground storey or a basement storey only. (a separated part which consists of a ground storey only, with a roof to which access is just for repair or maintenance, may be treated as a part of a single storey building). See Appendix C, Diagram 36 for number of storeys in a building or separated part

Storey - See B1 (1.0.9)

Storey exit - See BI (1.0.9)

Suspended ceiling (fire protecting) - See Appendix A, Table A3, for different types

Thermoplastic material - See Appendix A, paragraph A14

Travel distance - See B1(1.0.9)

Unprotected area - See B4 (4.0.2)

Wall - (for the purpose of B2) See B2 (2.0.7)

Appendix E
Assessment of Risk in Industrial and Storage Buildings

Assessment of Fire Risk and Associated Life Risk

E1 As premises covered by this Document can vary greatly in size and layout, the risk of fire can also vary considerably from one situation to another, particularly in industrial and storage buildings where widely differing processes may be carried out and hazardous substances are stored or used. It is essential, therefore, that the fire precautions to be provided should be determined having regard to all relevant circumstances.

For the purpose of the guidance in this Document, two categories of risk are used for industrial and storage buildings. These are described as:

Industrial (Purpose Group 6)

(a) normal risk, and

(b) high risk.

Storage (Purpose Group 7(a))

(a) normal risk, and

(b) high risk.

Industrial and storage buildings for the purpose of the relevant guidance should be treated as "normal risk" unless identified, by reasons of the criteria outlined in this Appendix, as being "high risk".

It should be noted that it is not possible to set out precise rules or other criteria that will be adequate to clearly establish the risk category in all cases. It is possible, however, to describe in broad terms the kind of factors which will need to be considered to determine if a building can be described as "high risk".

The details contained in the following paragraphs should be treated as broad indicators. It does not necessarily follow that the presence (or indeed the absence) of one of the factors mentioned in the description of the "high risk" category inevitably means that the premises or part of the premises have to be placed in that category. It is likely that in many industrial and storage buildings there will be a mixture of risks. It is emphasised that all factors should be considered.

At the building design stage, it may be difficult to determine the exact nature of the processes or storage involved. However, the basis for the assessment should always be established in order to provide for adequate fire safety measures.

Attention is drawn to obligations under the Fire Services Act, 1981 and the Safety, Health and Welfare at Work Act, 1989. The measures to be provided under the Building Regulations are intended to cater for fire safety in buildings generally and may not be adequate for the range of process and industrial hazards that could arise when the building is in use. The measures provided may therefore need to be supplemented accordingly.

Assessment of High Risk

E2 Factors which lead to the assessment of premises or parts of the premises as being of high risk include the following:-

(a) the presence of materials likely, when ignited, to cause the rapid spread of fire, smoke or fumes. The materials may be solid, liquid, or gaseous and as well as the normal forms may be present as dust, spray, mist or vapour;

(b) the presence of highly flammable or explosive materials (other than in small quantities);

(c) certain areas which, due to their function, may present a greater risk of fire occurring and developing than elsewhere such as manufacturing processes handling highly flammable liquids;

(d) the storage of hazardous goods or materials and the storage of vehicles containing hazardous goods or materials;

(e) manufacturing, processing, repairing, cleaning, washing, breaking up or otherwise treating any hazardous substance.

Hazardous Materials

E3 Materials falling within the following general descriptions should be considered as hazardous materials:

(i) Explosives;

(ii) Compressed or liquified gases;

(iii) Flammable liquids with a flash point below 65°C including whisky or other spirituous liquor;

(iv) Substances which becomes dangerous by interaction with either water or air;

(v) Corrosive substances;

(vi) Oxidising agents;

(vii) Substances liable to spontaneous combustion;

(viii) Substance that changes or decomposes readily giving out heat when doing so;

(ix) Combustible solid substance with a flash point less than 120°C;

(ix) Any substance likely to spread fire by flowing from one part of a building to another.

The above list is not necessarily exhaustive. There are a number of classification systems for hazardous materials such as the U.S Department of Transport (DOT) or that produced by the United Nations Committee of Experts for the Transport of Dangerous Goods which may also be used for this purpose.

Appendix F
Reference Standards

Standards referred to in BI

British Standards Institution

BS 5306
Fire extinguishing installations and equipment on premises

Part 1: 1976
Hydrant systems, hose reels and foam inlets

Part 2:
Specification for sprinkler systems

BS 5395
Stairs, ladder and walkways

Part 2:
Code of Practice for the design of helical and spiral stairs

BS 5499: Part 1: 1990 AMD 7444
Specification for fire safety signs

BS 5588
Fire precautions in the design, construction and use of buildings

Part 1: 1990 AMD 7840
Code of practice for residential buildings

Part 2: 1985 AMD 6478
Code of practice for shops. AMD 5555; AMD 6239

Part 3: 1983 AMD 5556; AMD 5825; AMD 6160
Code of practice for office buildings

Part 4: 1978 AMD 5377
Code of practice for smoke control in protected escape routes using pressurisation

Part 6: 1991
Code of practice for places of assembly

Part 8: 1988
Code of practice for means of escape for disabled people

Part 9: 1989
Code of practice for ventilation and air conditioning ductwork

Part 10
Code of practice for shopping complexes

BS 5720: 1979
Code of practice for mechanical ventilation and air conditioning in buildings

BS 5725:
Emergency exit devices
Part 1: 1995
Specification for panic bolts and panic latches mechanically operated by a horizontal push-bar.

BS 5839
Fire detection and alarm systems for buildings

Part 1: 1988 AMD 6317; AMD 6874
Code of practice for system design, installation and servicing

Part 6: 1995
Code of practice for the design and installation of fire detection and alarm systems in dwellings

BS 5906: 1980 (1987)
Code of practice for storage and on-site treatment of solid waste from buildings

BS 5925: 1991
Code of practice for ventilation principles and designing for natural ventilation

BS 6387: 1994
Specification for performance requirements for cables required to maintain circuit integrity under fire conditions

National Standards Authority of Ireland

I.S. 3217 : 1989
Code of practice for emergency lighting

I.S. 3218: 1989
Fire Detection and Alarm Systems

I.S./EN 671
Fixed fire fighting systems

Part 1: 1995 Hose reels with semi-rigid hose

Standards referred to in B2

British Standards Institution

BS 476
Fire tests on building materials and structures

Part 6: 1989
Method of test for fire propogation for products

Part 7:1987 (1993) AMD 7612
Method for the classification of the surface spread of flame of products

BS 2782
Methods of testing plastics

BS 5438: 1976 AMD 3595
Methods of test for flammability of vertically oriented textile fabrics and fabric assemblies subject to a small igniting flame

Standards referred to in B3

British Standards Institution

BS 4514: 1983 AMD 4517; AMD 5584
Specification for unplasticized PVC soil and ventilating pipes, fittings and accessories

BS 5255: 1989
Specification for plastic waste pipe and fittings

BS 5306
Fire extinguishing installations and equipment on premises

Part 2: 1990
Specification for sprinkler systems

BS 5588
Fire precautions in the design, construction and use of buildings

Part 9: 1989
Code of practice for ventilation and air-conditioning ductwork

Part 10:
Code of practice for shopping complexes

Standards referred to in B4

British Standards Institution

BS 476
Fire tests on building materials and structures

Part 3: 1958
External fire exposure roof tests

BS 5306
Fire extinguishing installations and equipment on premises

Part 2: 1990
Sprinkler systems

Standards referred to in B5

British Standards Institution

BS 336: 1989
Specification for fire hose couplings and ancillary equipment

BS 750: 1984
Specification for underground fire hydrants and surface box frames and covers

BS 3251 : 1976(1993) AMD 6736
Specification Indicator plates for fire hydrants and emergency water supplies

BS 5306
Fire extinguishing installations and equipment on premises

Part 1: 1988
Hydrant systems, hose reels and foam inlets

BS 5588
Fire precautions in the design, construction and use of buildings

Part 5: 1991 AMD 7196
Code of practice for firefighting stairways and lifts

Standards referred to in Appendix A

British Standards Institution

BS 476
Fire tests on building materials and structures

Part 3: 1958
External fire exposure roof test

Part 4: 1970 (1984)
Non-combustibility test for materials

Part 6: 1968
Fire propagation test for materials

Part 6: 1981 (1989)
Method of test for fire propagation for products

Part 7: 1987 AMD 6249; AMD 7030; AMD 7612
Surface spread of flame tests for materials

Part 11: 1982 (1988)
Method for assessing the heat emission from building products

Part 20: 1987 AMD 6487
Method for determination of the fire resistance of elements of construction (general principles)

Part 21: 1987
Methods for determination of the fire resistance of loadbearing elements of construction

Part 22: 1987
Methods for determination of the fire resistance of non-loadbearing elements of construction

Part 23: 1987
Methods for determination of the contribution of components to the fire resistance of a structure

Part 24: 1987
Method for determination of the fire resistance of ventilation ducts

BS 2782
Methods of testing plastics

BS 2782: Part 1
Thermal properties

Methods 120A to 120E: 1976
Determination of the Vicat softening temperature of thermoplastics

Method 508A
Performs so that the test flame extinguishes before the first mark, and the duration of flaming or afterglow does not exceed 5 seconds following removal of the burner

BS 5306 : Part 2: 1990
Specification for sprinkler systems

BS 6336: 1982
Guide to development and presentation of fire tests and their use in hazard assessment

PD 6520: 1988
Guide to fire test methods for building materials and elements of construction

National Standards Authority of Ireland

I.S. 325: Part 2: 1995
Code of Practice for the use of masonry, Part 2. Masonry construction

Standards referred to in Appendix B

British Standards Institution

BS 476
Fire tests on building materials and structures

Part 22: 1987
Methods for determination of the fire resistance of non-loadbearing elements of construction

Section 31.1: 1983
Methods of measuring smoke penetration through doorsets and shutter assemblies. Measurement under ambient temperature conditions

BS 5499
Fire safety signs, notices and graphic symbols

Part 1: 1990
Specification for fire safety signs

BS 5588
Fire precautions in the design, construction and use of buildings

Part 4: 1978
Code of practice for smoke control in protected escape routes using pressurization

BS 8214: 1990
Code of Practice for fire door assemblies with non-metallic leaves

Appendix G
Reference Publications

Other Publications referred to

B0

* The SFPE Handbook of Fire Protection Engineering. Society of Fire Protection Engineers, Boston, USA and National Fire Protection Association, USA

* Mathematical fire modelling and its application to fire safety design. Building Research Establishment (BR 223)

* Fire Modelling. Building Research Establishment, (Digest 367)

* Fire Models: a Guide for Fire Prevention Officers. Home Office Fire Research and Development Group (6/93)

* Fire protection in old buildings and historic town centres. The Fire Protection Association, London

* Fire protection measures for the Royal Palaces (The Bailey Report). Department of National Heritage, London

* Heritage under fire. A guide to the protection of historic buildings. The United Kingdom Working Party on fire safety in historic buildings

BI

* S.I. No. 249 of 1985 Fire Safety in Places of Assembly (Ease of Escape) Regulations

* Technical Guidance Document J - Heat Producing Appliances

* Technical Guidance Document K - Stairways, ladders, ramps and guards

* Technical Guidance Document M - Access for Disabled People

* Design principles for smoke ventilation in enclosed shopping centres. BRE, [1990]. (Revision of Smoke control methods in enclosed shopping complexes of one or more storeys. A design summary. (BRE) HMSO, 1979)

* Firecode Health Technical Memorandum 81, Fire Precautions in new hospitals, 1996

* Firecode Health Technical Memorandum 92, Alarm and detection systems, 1996

* Building Bulletin 7. Fire and the design of educational buildings. Department of Education and Science (United Kingdom) HMSO, 1988

* National Rules for electrical installations (ET 101). The Electro Technical Council of Ireland

* Fire Services Act, 1981

* Safety, Health and Welfare at Work Act, 1989

* S.I. No. 132 of 1995. Safety, Health and Welfare at Work (Signs) Regulations, 1995

B2

* Code of Practice for Fire Safety of Furnishings and Fittings in Places of Assembly. Department of the Environment

B3

* Design principles for smoke ventilation in enclosed shopping centres. Building Research Establishment (BR 186)

* Design approachs for smoke control in atrium buildings, Building Research Establishment (BR 258)

B4

* External fire spread: building separation and boundary distances. Building Research Establishment, (BR 187)

* The behaviour of steel portal frames in boundary conditions (PO 87) (available from the Steel Construction Institute, Silwood Park, Ascot, Berks, SL5 7QN)

* Fire and steel construction: the behaviour of steel portal frames in boundary conditions (PO87). The Steel Construction Institute

Appendix A

* Guidelines for the construction of fire-resisting structural elements. Building Research Establishment (BR 128)

* Increasing the fire resistance of existing timber floors. Building Research Establishment (Digest 208)

* Fire Grading of Buildings, Part 1. General Principles and Structural Precautions. Post-War Building Studies No. 20. HMSO, 1946

* Rules for the construction and installation of fire-break doors and shutters. Loss Prevention Council 1988

* Fire protection for structural steel in buildings. Association of Specialist Fire Protection Contractors and Manufacturers 1992

* Fire protection of structural steel in buildings, Association of Specialist Fire Protection Contractors and Manufacturers Ltd. (ASFPCM), 1992

Appendix B

* Code of practice for hardware essential to the optimum performance of timber doorsets. The Association of Builders' Hardware Manufacturers, 1983